AFRICAN WRITERS SERIES

General Editor · Chinua Achebe

73

North African Writing

AFRICAN WRITERS SERIES

North African Writing

Selected, translated,
and with an Introduction
by Len Ortzen

HEINEMANN EDUCATIONAL BOOKS
LONDON · IBADAN · NAIROBI

Heinemann Educational Books Ltd
48 Charles Street, London WIX 8AH
PMB 5205 Ibadan · POB 25080 Nairobi
EDINBURGH MELBOURNE TORONTO
AUCKLAND HONG KONG SINGAPORE

SBN 435 90073 0

First published 1970

Set in Monotype Fournier
and printed in Great Britain by
Cox & Wyman Ltd
London, Fakenham and Reading

CONTENTS

ACKNOWLEDGEMENTS

I wish to thank the following publishers and authors for permission to use copyright material:

Les Editions du Seuil for three stories from *Le Talisman* by Mohammed Dib; for a story from *Le Chapelet d'Ambre* by Ahmed Sefrioui; for extracts from *Le Polygone Étoilé* by Kateb Yacine; and for extracts from *Les Chemins qui Montent* by Mouloud Feraoun.

Les Editions Denoël for two stories from *De Tous Les Horizons*, by Driss Chraibi.

Les Editions Julliard for a story from *Peloton de Tête* by Hacène Farouk Zehar; for a chapter from *Les Impatients* by Assia Djebar; and for extracts from *Je t'offrirai une Gazelle* by Malek Haddad.

Librairie Plon for an extract from *Le Sommeil du Juste* by Mouloud Mammeri.

My thanks are also due to the Cresset Press, publishers of the English edition of *Le Sommeil du Juste* under the title *The Sleep of the Just*, for permission to make use of my translation of this novel. Acknowledgements are also made to the Editor and Proprietors of *The London Magazine*, in which my translation of 'Four Trunks' first appeared.

In addition, I am grateful to Mr Denys Johnson-Davies and Mr Tawfiq Sayigh, respectively editors of the now, alas, defunct Arabic magazines *Aswat* and *Hiwar* (Beirut), for publishing reviews and articles of mine, on which I have drawn for my Introduction.

INTRODUCTION

In the early nineteen-fifties, creative African writers of several countries began to publish their work in London or Paris, according to the language in which they wrote. It was a slow trickle of books at first, and most of them came from French writers. Their work met with almost immediate recognition and three were awarded French literary prizes, unlike the work of Africans who published in London. But this was probably due to the higher status of the creative writer in France; and also to the fact that the French expect him to appear wherever their language is spoken, whereas the British are always rather surprised when he emerges.

The majority of these early writers published in Paris were Algerians, four in number. Only one of them, Mohammed Dib, is still producing books, nearly twenty years later; but younger writers have appeared, from Morocco as well as Algeria, so that this North African school of writers is now firmly established and has made a considerable and distinct contribution to West European literature. The school even has its martyr; though only in the loosest manner can these North African writers be called a 'school'. Each writer has worked in creative isolation from the others, and each has an individual style and distinctive outlook – as will be seen on reading through the following selection from their books. All, however, have in common an urge to express the aspirations, the bewilderment and resentment of the mass of their fellow-countrymen. Moreover their books are essentially products of the Arab world, even though the medium of expression is the French language.

It may be only a coincidence that three of the early writers,

Mouloud Mammeri, Mouloud Feraoun, and Malek Ouary, were all born in Kabylia, a mountainous region of Algeria ideal for guerrilla warfare. Their first books appeared at a time when the Algerian Arabs were beginning to revolt against the French; but only one book – Mammeri's second novel, *Le Sommeil du Juste* – can properly be called a novel of revolt, though not of hate. All three writers began, like most writers everywhere, by drawing upon their own experiences and seeking inspiration from the life around them. This is also true of Mohammed Dib; though most of the action in his first novel, *La Grande Maison*, takes place in an overcrowded tenement; whereas the three Kabylians set their stories in the countryside, in mountain villages.

All four writers came from poor, peasant families, and obtained their French education by scholarship. Three began their working lives as school-teachers; the other, Malek Ouary, worked for Algiers Radio. In the early nineteen-fifties, all were still in their thirties and had never left their native land, except Mammeri who had served with the French Army in Europe during the latter part of the Second World War. Writing was for them a part-time occupation. They worked on a small canvas, with a limited aim – to reveal within an artistic framework the mentality and real life of the Algerian Arabs, in a way that no stranger could do. But the characters in their novels, with very few exceptions, are unformed, furtive and slippery; to grasp them is like trying to grapple with a jelly. What does emerge most strikingly from these early novels is the great contrast and wide gap between the young, French-educated generation of Algerian Arabs and that of their parents, still confined within the ancient customs and superstitions of their ancestors. Yet, far from sneering at the survival of these ancestral prejudices and antiquated ways of thought, when these matters appear on some of the pages the reader can discern more than a trace of nostalgia. Life was simple then, straightforward and clear-cut; honour was all, not to believe in God was blasphemy. Now all is confusion: 'Nothing is respected any more, and everything is equal to everything else,' the old father in *Le Sommeil du Juste* complains when writing –

with the help of the public scribe – to his son. And he continues: 'This war (1940) has brought back to Ighzer all our men who had emigrated to France, all those who left us so long ago that we had forgotten about them. They have come back with habits and a way of speaking which make my heart bleed to see and hear. . . . Come back home, even if you have no money. I'd rather you were here, because then I shall know that like our forefathers you can still distinguish good from evil, that you're not likely one day to come back to Ighzer blundering into everything like a blind man because you can no longer see the true light, confused as a child with no sense of proportion, and kicking everything aside because contact with the West would have made you become like them, thinking only of the delights of the flesh, as though in a wilderness emptied of men your desires alone mattered. I'm expecting you then.'

This additional theme of the lack of comprehension between Arabs who have been to work in France and the peasants who have never left their villages runs through all Feraoun's three novels. In his unaffected, modest, almost naïve style, he wrote of everyday village affairs without any striving for picturesque effect. We come to understand something of the life of his village better than that of Dib's crowded streets; a village where a sense of honour is all important, where the major worry of marrying off a daughter is then succeeded by the fear of her being repudiated.

One looked forward to the work of these writers increasing in stature and depth; and Mammeri's second novel was a profoundly disturbing work, later published in translation in Britain and America. However, both Ouary and Mammeri dropped out of the literary scene; and Feraoun's life was cut short. He was assassinated by French terrorists in March 1962. A few months later his Diary for the years 1955–62 was published. It had been written in school exercise books, as a precaution, and Feraoun had kept them hidden among a pile of his pupils' books. No writer has conveyed what life in Algeria was really like for ordinary Arabs during the War of Independence so much as

Feraoun does in his Diary. The entries bring home to the reader the gradual changes in atmosphere as conditions deteriorated and violence began to meet with violence. He himself was threatened by both sides. The changes in himself are noted too, the inner feelings and tormented conscience of a humanist who is fond of his country and aware of its miseries.

'The representatives of France, here, have always treated me as an enemy since the troubles began, yet they would like me to act like a good French patriot – simply out of gratitude because France has made a headmaster and a writer of me . . . as though all that were a generous gift I'd only had to hold out my hand for. As though in return I ought to support the French cause to the detriment of my own people, who may be in error but who suffer and die . . . I'm simply asked to die as a traitor, and then I should have paid my debt . . .'

An entry in April 1958, a few weeks before the French Army in Algeria seized power, mentions a meeting with Albert Camus:

'Camus came here yesterday. We chatted for a couple of hours, quite frankly and simply. I at once felt as much at ease with him as with E. Roblès [the French–Algerian author]. He has that same brotherly warmth . . . his pity for the suffering people is great, but he knows, alas, that pity and love no longer have any power over the evil which is killing and destroying . . .'

Feraoun was moved from his village to a school in Algiers, and there he became active in caring for his fellow-Kabylians in need. He was appointed inspector of Social Welfare centres. More than once, he refused to lend his name to one side or the other, and this again brought him menaces from both.

The last page of his Diary is written by his eldest son. It tells of the last evening that Feraoun spent with his family. The following morning he was at a welfare committee meeting in Algiers when French terrorists broke into the room, took Feraoun and five others outside and riddled them with bullets.

Mouloud Feraoun is buried in his native village of Tizi-Hibel, among the Kabylian mountains, where he learnt to read and write. No better portrait can be drawn of him than the one that emerges from the pages of his last book, his Diary: the portrait of a liberal humanist, a generous-minded man who loved all his fellows.

Mohammed Dib continued, and still continues, to produce novels, short stories, and poems. Since his first book was published in 1952 he has developed in a remarkable way, from being a realistic, straightforward writer to one with a poetic vision and an impressionistic technique. He was born in 1920 at Tlemcen, near the Algerian-Moroccan frontier, and found great difficulty in earning a living after leaving college. He had a succession of jobs – primary school-teacher, carpet-weaver, railway worker – before becoming a reporter on a local paper. Then he began contributing articles and short stories to Algerian French-language magazines, and started on his trilogy, *Algérie* (of which *La Grande Maison* is the first volume), which he completed in 1957 with *Le Métier à Tisser*. It is a semi-auto-biographical work, about an Arab lad's progress in life, written in a beautiful, flowing style but with little development of character. In 1959, Dib left the town where he was born and had lived for nearly forty years, and went to settle in the south of France. This move obviously had a profound effect upon him and his writing. In the next novel that he published, *Un Été Africain*, he was writing outside himself for the first time. The book is concerned with several Arab families of different social levels, all leading separate lives that do not touch, like parallel lines on the same page – the page being the town they all live in during the threatening heat of a North African summer. The family and story which take up most of the book are that of Mouktar Rai, a civil servant, and his wife and daughter and old mother. They are always, so it seems, sitting drinking tea in their patio where the fountain plays without making the hot air any the fresher. Every evening Mouktar's brother comes to join them. They all say the same things each time, go through the same motions, as in a play by Chekhov. Yet, even here, the changing outside world intrudes. The daughter, Zakya, who has finished her studies, wants to be a school-teacher. Her father says yes, then no. What then, complains Zakya, has been the use of my working hard and getting a diploma, if I'm going to finish up like other women? Then her grandmother bursts out: 'You see where your studies get you – lacking respect for us, your elders, who brought you into the world! Believe me, education makes you youngsters worse than you are naturally. You make me tired, with your martyred airs. Anyone would think you were being led to the slaughter-house, just because we talk of marrying you to someone!'

All Dib's characters in this book are affected to a slight or great degree by the struggle going on around them. Even as that is in suspense, so Dib shows the lives of his people in a state of suspense too.

Dib returned to semi-autobiographical writing with *Cours Sur La Rive Sauvage,* but all the action takes place in the narrator's head, in a sort of protracted nightmare. This novel was the first of the North African 'school' to be published after Algeria had attained independence; it is symbolic of the strained relationship between that country and France, being an impressionistic account of one Algerian's attempts to come to terms with France and the French. The narrator is about to be married to Radia, who appears as 'a glittering white incarnation of power'. 'She came towards me,' the narrator continues, 'and stabbed me in the chest. The shock, the surprise too, took my breath away. I waited to feel the pain, but none came. Then, with the same calm resolution, she stabbed me again, five times in all. It was useless to call on the people standing around, supposing that any of them would have raised a finger in my defence . . .'

Radia is symbolic of France or of Western civilization in general, and Dib has found that living in France is not quite what he had thought it would be.

The narrator goes off to another city, but he feels just as isolated and lonely. Now begins a series of incidents of seeing other women remarkably like Radia. He finds himself going along a corridor, past a line of bedrooms in each of which a woman is sleeping. Which is the real Radia and which are the imitations? Suddenly they all wake up, and begin making similar gestures one after the other. The conclusion is that Radia – the ideal – is split up, she is everywhere and nowhere. The only thing he can understand is Radia's regret that he is still looking for her. She shows him the empty masks which she must put on in order to appear in public.

One sees how it is. Mohammed Dib, with his French education, the acceptance of his books in France – and by then he had been awarded four French literary prizes for them – has built up an idealistic image of France for himself, and then finds that the reality is somewhat different. This has happened to many people before.

The techniques he employs in his recent novels are reminiscent of abstract painting. Indeed, *Qui Se Souvient de la Mer* was inspired by Picasso's painting *Guernica*. In this book, as in his latest, *La Danse du Roi*, Dib has returned to the theme of the futility of war – obviously the Algerian War of Independence, which continues to haunt him. Many of his short stories, too, are set in time of war. But Dib is not a partisan; his sympathies are with all people caught up in the horrors of war, and his stories could apply equally to the situation in Viet-Nam or Biafra. Although his characters are Arabs, they speak for people everywhere, especially the downtrodden and the under-privileged.

Dib, now the doyen of the North African Arabs who write in French, has published three collections of short stories, and this art-form may well be his best medium of expression. The three stories in this anthology show the development in style and technique of this important writer.

Two Moroccan writers, Ahmed Sefrioui and Driss Chraibi, had their first books published in Paris in the early nineteen-fifties. Their work is very different in style and content from that of the Algerian authors; and the books of the two themselves could hardly be less alike.

The elder, Sefrioui, was born at Fez in 1915, of Berber parents. He went to school there, first to the Koranic school and then to the French college, and lived there for many years,

working at the Arts and Crafts Institute, until moving to Rabat
to take charge of the State Tourist Office. His literary output has
been small, but his obvious love of the old crafts and their
dedicated practitioners shines through all his writing. The short
story reproduced here, 'The Earthenware Jar', has a typical
theme of the power of purity and beauty over evil. Sefrioui's
stories are more like parables, in which the real world soon blends
into a kind of fairyland. But it is the real world which always
triumphs – and for Ahmed Sefrioui the real world is the narrow,
busy streets of old Fez, the holy city that he loves, the world of
obscure, simple people, carpet-weavers and sandal-makers,
flower-sellers and masons, students and pilgrims and potters.
Sefrioui's people have a healthy philosophy of life, because
untouched by modern industrialism.

Driss Chraibi, the son of a wealthy merchant, was educated at
the French grammar school in Casablanca, then went to Paris
to study chemistry. That was in 1946, when he was twenty, and
he has lived in France almost continually since then. Twice
married, each time to a Frenchwoman, he scratches a living with
his pen, contributing articles and reviews to Moroccan period-
icals, working for the French Radio now and again – even working
in chemical laboratories when things get really tough – and
publishing a book every two or three years.

Chraibi is the most violent, despairing, and uncompromising
of these North African writers. His first book, *Le Passé Simple*,
conveys a hate of Islam, and was a reaction to the harsh Muslim
formalism he suffered from in childhood. His second book, *Les
Boucs* – an insulting name given to the North African Arabs
living in Paris – is a call for vengeance. It is a violent, one-sided
book, lacking in objectivity. But then revolt is Chraibi's religion
and he must choose extremes; he is in revolt against both the
West and the Orient – at least, so much emerges from these two
early books, written when in his twenties.

Since then, he has said in private that he hopes for a fusion of
the interests of the West and the Orient. And his third book,
L'Ane, is a more considered, more acute work than the earlier

two. It is short and more a parable than a novel, yet does more than other books to convey to us the inner struggles, indecision and bewilderment of the newly-awakened peoples of North Africa. Why have they been awakened? Chraibi asks for them. The ass belongs to an itinerant barber who, vaguely aware of the change around him, sells the animal and buys a modern set of hairdresser's instruments. The ass follows him about, braying to him to return to the good old days, until killed by a train that his ex-master is travelling on.

The barber says: 'I thought I was properly awake then. But it was not so. Look at this lorry of mine – I can hear it, see it, touch it. That's all I can do for the time being. I've been told what it's useful for, what its daily nourishment is, and so on – I understand all that perfectly, but I can't drive it. Like everyone else, I'm just a spectator.'

By continued literary expression, Chraibi seemed to have exorcized his demon of revolt. In his collection of short stories – two of which appear here – his style became firmer and more disciplined, his imaginative vision clearer and more penetrating. Chraibi's stories have something of the Oriental fable about them. The plot is always slight, but the tragic force of the writing and the peremptory tone of the voice behind it hold our attention. More, they awaken our conscience.

The lack of comprehension between Europeans and the peoples of newly-awakened countries is a constant theme in Chraibi's work, as it is with many of these North African writers. In his novel *Succession Ouverte* – probably the best book he has written – Chraibi is concerned, like Mohammed Dib, with the problems of adjusting to the standards of another country, another civilization. The narrator and chief character is a Moroccan Arab who has been living in France for sixteen years, having revolted against his father's way of life and gone off to assimilate Western civilization. When the story opens, he, Driss Ferdi – Driss Chraibi, as it might well be – is married to a Frenchwoman and has two children. Happily married, but personally anguished and torn because he has not been able to adjust himself. A telegram comes from Casablanca, informing him of the death of his father. He catches a plane, to get back in time for the funeral. As he raises the knocker of his parents' house, a telegraph boy hands him a telegram in his name. It is from his father, and it says: 'Welcome home'.

Driss is taken to the room where his father is laid out. There was another man there, Driss writes, with a blanket over his head. 'I removed the blanket, and the man looked at me for a long time in silence. His eyes were red. "Madini," I said. "My brother." He put a finger to his lips, and whispered, "Go and close his eyes. It was his last wish." '

Driss begins to wonder whether this is really the return of the prodigal son. But when his father's will is read — that is the major scene in the book, and a fine one — he finds that he has been left out of the inheritance. His name is not even mentioned by his father — and that is literal, for the will is on a tape-recorder.

Chraibi is adept at the ironic, cutting phrase, the 'throw-away line':

'Then came the turn of Camel (the son who had turned up for the funeral and the reading of the will merely in the hope of getting something). "The way you're made," said the voice, "you can't be happy without money. Seventy-five million, by crossed cheque. Don't forget the bank shuts at four. You've just got time to get there, before catching your train back."

'Camel started laughing. "What a blighter, our father! Do you want a cigarette?" He must have felt in the wrong pocket, for it was his watch that he pulled out.'

Succession Ouverte contains a parable in the Oriental manner — a meeting between the present and the past, a comment on Morocco faced with the problems of its emancipation. What has the new, modern generation inherited from the old, traditional one? And not only on Morocco, but on all the emergent countries. Driss Chraibi is one Arab writer whose vision sees further than his own country.

'My father is dead,' the narrator writes, 'and now I'm independent. But there's still ignorance, rooted traditions, misery, all those left-overs that prevent a man being free . . .'

Chraibi's most recent book, *Un Ami Viendra Vous Voir*, marks a new departure for him, inasmuch as all the characters are European. Briefly, it is about an unhappily married French-woman who is subjected to a TV interview, and afterwards murders her baby. A psychiatrist then tries to restore her mental health, and falls in love with her – as did the TV producer. It does not really succeed as a novel; for one thing, the characters never come to life. Nevertheless, the book shows another facet of Chraibi's talents, another indication that he more than any of the North African writers is capable of producing a really great work.

The next writers to appear on the literary scene, their first books being published in the late nineteen-fifties, were all Algerians: Malek Haddad, Kateb Yacine, and Assia Djebar. Only ten or a dozen years separate them from the previous writers – except from Chraibi, but he is an exception to every-thing – yet they are important years, for these three grew up during the Second World War and wrote their first books when the insurrection in Algeria was at its worst.

Malek Haddad was born at Constantine in 1927, went to the grammar school there, and then to the university of Aix-en Provence to study law. He settled in Algiers for a time, where he founded and helped edit the literary magazine *Progrès*. In 1955 he went to Paris, working for the Arabic service of the French Radio and contributing to various little magazines. His first published book was a volume of poems; and his first novel, *La Dernière Impression*, has poetry in it, a poetic prose that evokes the sadness of Algeria at that time.

The story is slight; it is more a symbol – as intended to be – of the strained relations between France and Algeria. Saïd is in love with a French girl. But she cannot bear life in Algeria and intends to take a job in France. Saïd is an engineer, and the bridge he has built must be blown, to hinder French military movements.

The author writes: 'But Saïd belongs to the young generation that must build bridges, bridges of goodwill. The generation that must stretch an arm out to the other side. Saïd's bridge was the last bridge. And his generation the last impression of the legend of centuries.'

The girl Saïd loves is killed by a stray bullet the day before she is due to leave Algeria for France. Saïd's bridge is blown. He joins the Arabs fighting in the mountains and is himself killed.

Haddad's second novel, published the following year, has the intriguing title *Je t'offrirai une Gazelle*. There are two pairs of lovers in this book, one couple in the Sahara desert and the other in the desert of Paris. Each is pursuing a mirage, an illusion of freedom, a fleeting gazelle. The extract in this anthology tells of the Sahara couple, of Moulay the lorry driver and Yaminata who is worth twenty white camels, and who asks him to bring her back a gazelle, a live one. In Paris, the narrator can only manage to present a stuffed gazelle to the young woman who has fallen in love with him.

The narrator – but it's the author himself, Haddad, writing about himself in the third person. And writing a book within a book, for the Paris part is about this young Frenchwoman, Gisèle, who works in a publisher's office and falls in love with the author of a book entitled *Je t'offrirai une Gazelle*.

All very complicated, the reader may well think. It's the desert that complicates things, the author would reply. The Sahara, he writes, surrounds an oasis with a thousand precautions; and while protecting it keeps it. The desert offers everything and gives nothing. And when you've left it you doubt its existence, its reality, even its unreality.

Haddad's writing sparkles like desert sand with what he himself calls a bitter optimism. Whatever he is writing about – and Haddad scorns all accepted forms of novel writing, darts from one scene to another apparently as the gazelle inspires him – we savour every line of his pungent prose. It is all crazy and beautiful; or beautifully crazy.

Finally, the author – or the narrator – finds that people are not interested in his book. They believe that a gazelle is a four-legged animal. So the author stops his book from being published – as we read on its printed page. Gisèle tells him he's completely crazy. But, as he says, it's a gazelle that one is really fighting for.

Haddad is no doubt saying that the desert, his desert, is life itself, and that we get out of it what we put into it.

His first two novels were experimental in form and highly original in matter. But it is the sadness of the author and not the unhappiness of his characters that touch the reader. As novels they fail. In his next books, Haddad turned to a more conventional form of novel-writing; and carried Feraoun's theme of the gap between the two generations of Algerians a stage further. But it is doubtful if Haddad is really a novelist. He still comes between his characters and the reader, and uses the novel as a medium for stating his own beliefs. Not that there is anything wrong with his beliefs:

'Faith built cathedrals,' says one of his characters in *L'Élève et La Leçon*, 'but necessity invented locomotives. Science and techniques leave me indifferent, if they have no soul . . . a soul has no need of an automatic lift to reach hell or paradise. Some day in the future a machine will be able to perform a surgical operation just as well as my friend. But the machine will never have the little smile of my friend, a smile in God's image.'

Then there is Kateb Yacine. What can one say of this enfant terrible? The publishers of his first book, *Nedjma*, published when he was twenty-seven, thought a prefatory warning to its readers was necessary. It is probably the first modern novel written in a European language that is still predominantly Arab in thought and construction. The book moves backwards and forwards in time, but with a cyclic motion – like a train shuttling on a circular railway. The reader can pick the book up at any point, at page 100 or 200, read on and then go to page one and continue – and still travel the whole way all right, with understanding, and get as much pleasure and interest from the journey.

The story – such as it is – is told through four friends who are all obsessed by their love for Nedjma, the central character. They know little about her origins, but gradually find out that she is

really the daughter of a Frenchwoman who had several lovers –
among them, the father of one of the four friends. The reader
realizes the allegorical nature of the theme, that Nedjma is a
symbol for Algeria herself. Nedjma, like Algeria, is not yet fully
formed; men still dispute over her creation.

Yacine seems obsessed by his subject matter, submerged in it.
Ideas and descriptions flow from his pen with a tense rhythm,
and throughout the book there is a dry, bitter humour not unlike
that of other North African writers. For example:

'It's a covered market we're building,' says one Algerian
workman to another. 'Yes,' the other replies, 'the town's paying
three-quarters of the cost. The rest is met by the State. Our boss
only supplies the material. His foreman gives the orders. We, the
workmen, we're not concerned with it. Some have died without
ever being sure of having worked at something. Even supposing
it's a solid project, who knows whether the covered market
won't turn out to be a police station?'

Much of the material is probably drawn from his own experiences. Kateb Yacine was born near Constantine in 1929. His
French education was interrupted when, at the age of sixteen, he
was arrested for taking part in anti-French demonstrations and
spent several months in prison. He worked as a reporter on an
Algiers newspaper for a time. On the death of his father in 1950,
Yacine went to France and earned a living at various unskilled
jobs, including a spell in the ricefields of the Camargue with
Malek Haddad. The two are of the same age and come from the
same part of Algeria.

While writing *Nedjma*, Yacine was also expressing himself
through the medium of drama; and his plays, like his books, are
highly original in form. His first play, *Le Cadavre Encerclé*, was
originally published in the Paris literary magazine *Esprit*. Three
years later, in 1958, the play was produced at an experimental
theatre in Brussels; and the following year the same company
gave two performances of it in Paris. It was then published in
book form, together with two other one-act plays by Yacine,
under the title *Le Cercle des Représailles*.

As with his novels, the content of his plays is an expression of troubled Algeria. The characters are symbols too. But the important thing is that this North African writer has renewed classical Greek tragedy. As the Greek dramatists did, Yacine makes effective use of masks, of choruses and chorus leaders; but not just to mark the end of a scene and to comment on the action, but to enter into the play and heighten the action. He has no curtain-drop, but a blackout and the beating of a gong; he uses the minimum of means, of stage props, to produce a maximum of intensity. His stage directions for one play read: 'The scenery is reduced to a minimum, just two trees and a stretch of wall to serve as a film-screen. The lights go out, then flash on again. A man is seen asleep on the matting. His wife is seated in a corner with a packet of dates in front of her, lit by a candle.'

By the use of modern effects, of lighting, film projection and amplifiers, Yacine adds to the dramatic intensity of his scenes. In the tragedy called *Les Ancêtres Redoublent de Férocité*, the shape of a vulture, the bird of death and the messenger of the ancestors, is thrown on to the wall that serves as a film-screen. All else is in darkness while a distant voice, the voice of the vulture, is heard, punctuated by the beating of a gong. In the following scenes, the vulture keeps reappearing and adds to the drama of the moment by circling smoothly over the action on the stage – when this is to its approval – or by beating its wings furiously, because unable to intervene, when it disapproves.

It is not too much to say that a decade ago Kateb Yacine created a new art form by combining cinema, radio, and stage techniques. Unfortunately, his plays do not appear to be commercially valid, and are unlikely to be performed other than in small, experimental theatres.

His recent novel, *Le Polygone Étoilé*, is – he tells us frankly – another form of the same work; of a work that first appeared as a poem, *Nedjma* (published in *Mercure de France* when he was nineteen), then as the play *Un Cadavre Encerclé* and then the novel *Nedjma*. Only the content is different, and the work increases in stature each time. And Yacine's style has become

brisk, nervous, jerky, as though he is impatient to get it all down.
He jumps from one scene to another, and leaves it to the reader
to bridge the gap. The episodes are interspersed with poems,
newspaper reports, a brief biography of Ibn Khaldoun, even a
satirical playlet on the French conquest of Algeria in 1840. A
collage, in fact. The overall impression is a book bulging with
imagery, ideas and symbolic incidents – but lacking in disciplined
control.

Assia Djebar has her material very much under control, but
she works on a smaller scale and on more conventional lines. Her
novels, which really are novels, take us into the enclosed world
of Arab women, and are as much books of revolt as any by her
male compatriots – but of female revolt against restrictive
customs.

Assia Djebar is the only woman novelist in North Africa, so
she is ploughing a lonely furrow. The men writers have
no problems when portraying Arab women characters: their
place is traditional, they are second-class citizens without a
doubt.

Outside the city, Algeria looks like a single-sex State. The old
rules apply more strictly here than in most Arab countries;
women are veiled, and always subject to some male relative. The
married woman's lot is babies and more babies. The part that
women played in the War of Independence had earned them the
right to a higher status in the free State, but this has not material-
ized. The increasing number of girls at school and university is a
hopeful portent; but employment, the usual path to independence
for European women, is very limited for Algerian women
because of the massive unemployment of men.

Assia Djebar went to war against the subjection of Algerian
women long before her country achieved independence. When
that happened, she had already published three novels and was
only twenty-six. She was born in Algiers in 1936 of a middle-
class, traditionalist Muslim family. After attending grammar
school in Algiers she went to Paris to read history at the
Sorbonne. Having obtained her degree, she returned to North

Africa and taught first at Tunis and then at Rabat University, combining an academic career with her literary achievements. She is now married, and lives most of the time in France.

Her first novel was translated into English and published in Britain and the United States; but the best of her four novels is the second, *Les Impatients*. The character of Delila, the heroine, who narrates the story, is subtly revealed and developed in depth. She makes the acquaintance of a young man, Salim, at a house where she goes to discuss with other girls the emancipation of Arab women. In order to meet him in the town, she has to invent lies to get permission from her stepmother, Lella, and her brother to leave the house for a few hours. Salim confesses his love for her. Delila continues to defy her brother and step-mother, especially as she suspects that Lella has a secret. Salim unwittingly reveals it to her – he was for a time her stepmother's lover. Delila follows Salim to Paris, but she cannot stand his jealous ways and his possessiveness, which remind her too much of the life she believed she had escaped from; and so she returns home, wiser and with a deeper understanding of life. Delila is the representative of a young, courageous generation in full evolution.

Assia Djebar's later books are more ambitious but do not succeed so well. She seems more occupied with technique than with her characters, which are more numerous than in her earlier novels. But she is still greatly concerned with the restricted lives of Arab women and the attempts of some of them to escape into a larger world. She portrays most of her men characters as egotistical and their womenfolk as submissive. Beneath the sympathetic and sensitive writing the reader gets the impression that the authoress is really just as annoyed with the women as with their masters -- if not more so – for this state of affairs.

Assia Djebar, still in her early thirties and with four novels to her credit, gives strong indications of being the mainstay of North African writing.

She is not, however, the youngest of the North African authors; there are three others who are a few years junior to her, and each in his way gives promise of adding to the diversity of this literary output from North Africa.

Hacène Farouk Zehar, a young Algerian, has chosen the short story as the medium in which to begin his writing career. His collection, *Peloton de Tête*, contains four short stories and on long one – and the latter would be a lot better if it were as short as the others. Zehar lacks stamina at the moment, but he already has great assurance of style and his work is stamped with an original outlook. His stories – and they are indeed stories, not just character studies – are a kind of science fiction with an underlying theme of the insecurity of this day and age. All the stories are written in the first person and the present tense, which of course adds to the immediacy and heightens the dramatic element. One of them, *Foi d'Ivrogne*, appears in the following pages.

Mohammed Khair-Eddine is a young Moroccan who now lives in Paris and contributes to literary magazines and to *Présence Africaine*. He has published two short books of literary experimentalism, and his work has been compared, inevitably, to that of Kateb Yacine. His first book, *Agadir*, was awarded the Prix des Enfants Terribles, which would seem to be most appropriate. He is an intellectual, impressionistic writer, hard to penetrate; a single sentence in his book sometimes covers several pages; there is blank verse – some of it reminiscent of passages from the Koran – and playlets; but he retains firm control of his theme, the identification of the present generation with its forbears. However, he is essentially a poet, and recently published a collection of poems which are very *avant-garde*.

With Mourad Bourboune, one is back on surer ground; though both his novels are cyclic in construction, with the action moving back and forth in time and the episodes being circles within a circle, stories within stories. His books are set in Algeria – the first, during the insurrection – and he writes with great verve and ironic humour about life in a Casbah and its assortment of characters, creating them in the round and playing off one against another.

Bourboune wrote his first novel at twenty-three, when he was studying in Paris for a degree. His early schooling was at Constantine, but the Algerian war caused him to be sent to Tunis before going to complete his education in Paris.

These younger North African writers, with their higher French education, and living in France as they do, would appear to have a special problem: either to identify themselves with French traditions of writing and seek French subject-matter or to return to their original sources. Can they become assimilated in the French literary scene and yet retain that distinctive North African flavour which has so far heightened their work? That, at least, is what they seem to be striving after.

The twelve writers reviewed here do not, of course, represent all the literature from North Africa. There are a number of writers in Arabic; though the majority of these are in countries to the east. In an anthology of contemporary Arabic writers, published in French translation a few years ago, the bulk of those represented came from Egypt and the Lebanon. The reason for this is because the Arab literary renaissance – the *nahd'â* – originated chiefly in the East, in the latter part of the nineteenth century; it was not felt nearly so much in the Maghreb (Tunisia, Algeria, and Morocco), where French influence was strong. Moreover, the Arabic writers are inward-looking and prefer to concentrate on the microscopic, chiefly through the medium of the short story or descriptive sketch. They cannot be said to have the international importance of the North African Arabs who write in French. It is they, conscious of their wider audience, who are the more militant and have the greater range. They are also conscious of belonging at once to their own people and to French civilization, and obviously feel the tension in their blood and bones.

Len Ortzen

MOHAMMED DIB

The Provider of all Good Gifts

That old scoundrel, Karmoni! Right now, he must be driving a hard bargain with the Devil for his soul. Even in hell, where I'm sure he's gone, he must be trying to make something out of the situation – a new one for him, but not unexpected. And there can be no doubt that he'll succeed, one way or another – if he hasn't done so already! A craftier black-marketeer and more resourceful old fox has never been known in our town, which has always had a good many. He drank away a fortune, amassed by means he was never too particular about, and then died. I don't suppose he minded. I mean that he had the satisfaction of not leaving a penny of his own.

However, there was someone who did bear him a grudge – Omar Douidi, the sexton, the man who dug his grave and who was one of his friends. Omar Douidi will always bear him ill-will.

'Every night,' he declared, 'I hear Karmoni whimpering as he's given the bastinado. He swears he's innocent. But he'll end up by confessing, the dog! There are too many people ready to bear witness against him, and he's caused too much misery.'

'Why do you and people like you,' Moulay Soltan was asked, 'always hang round that blackguard Karmoni like bees round a pot of honey? What pleasure can you find in his stupid talk?'

'So long as he buys us drinks he can say what he likes. No one listens to him.'

Karmoni once told the following story to his cronies:

'I used to go home drunk every night . . .'

(I should interject that if someone had thought of pointing out that his habit had not changed, the rash individual would have suffered from Karmoni's lordly vanity, and in a most disagreeable manner – not another drink would have been offered him.)

'I used to go home drunk every night, and when I found myself in front of an old grandfather-clock in my bedroom I would take the five thousand franc notes from the inside pocket of my jacket and, without knowing what I was doing, stuff them into the case of the clock, saying, "Here, monster, eat up!" I must have done this every night for a long time. But I re-membered nothing the following morning – it had all gone completely from my head, as you might expect. I'd gone home so drunk that I couldn't have told a cat from an elephant! Then one day my wife told me that the grandfather-clock had stopped. "Stopped?" I said. "Well, it's old. It needs a rest!" But you know what women are when they happen to get an idea into their head. They're so surprised that in order to convince themselves they have to let the whole world know of it. I tried turning a deaf ear, but she wouldn't let the matter drop and got on at me about that clock morning, noon and night. She had made up her mind that the mechanism which dated from our earliest forbears had to be repaired! Finally, I went to see if I could do something to it, just to have some peace. Sure enough, the pendulum was stuck. So I gave the clock a kick. It still wouldn't go. I opened the case where the weights and things are, to try to find out what had happened inside. And what did I see but a pile of five thousand franc notes! There were so many and they were jammed so tight that they'd completely stopped the works. I shouted to my wife: "Quick, bring some cushion-covers! We'll fill them with this paper!" She came, took one look and almost fainted. Then she started singing out: "How did all this wealth get there? All this wealth! . . . May God guard us. . . . It's *those others* – the spirits – they've been here!" And she's a woman who never raises her voice except to complain! My word, she was raving all right! I suddenly remembered what I had done. "Idiot," I said. "It was I who threw those notes in there when I came home drunk. Me, and nobody else!" She looked me up and down. "You expect me to believe that? Well, I won't! It was *those others*." And she gave me a knowing wink. I couldn't get over it. There was no convincing her that I was at the bottom of this joke. "All right, have it your own way," I said for the sake of peace and quiet. "It was the spirits." We filled several cushions with the notes, and the clock started to go again.'

When Karmoni left that café with his faithful followers to go and drink in another, he gathered up a couple of fried fish, some stuffed snails and olives that had been served with their drinks and wrapped them up in banknotes.

He said to them one day: 'You, for instance, you want this war to end. But you'll never find me thinking that. And it's in your interests, too, that the war should last as long as possible.'

They looked at him in silence. At last someone asked: 'Could you tell us why?'

'Because while it lasts, you will always be able to drink at my expense!'

There can be no doubt that he made money out of the war. So much, even, that he did not know what to do with it all. He launched into schemes which became so complicated that he was the first to lose his bearings, and he trusted to luck to see him through. He supplied food to the French Army, but his lorries always carried a few crates of weapons, hidden between the baskets of tomatoes and courgettes, which were delivered to agents of the Liberation Front while on the way from one town to another. The other side could hardly have been blind to this little game. He probably gave the French information to balance things up. The fact remains that the money rolled in and was as quickly thrown away, though not without a little of it falling into the hands of a number of poor wretches round and about the town, saving them from going hungry. So when his body was found one morning riddled with bullets, there was general consternation. The day of his funeral was a day of public mourning. No honest citizen had ever been accompanied to his last resting-place by a cortège so impressive in size and solemnity as was Karmoni. The French authorities were represented by high officials and the army supplied a guard of honour. But people in the know claimed that leaders of the Liberation Front were also among those following the coffin. However, everyone took it for granted that neither of the two opposing sides was implicated or could have given orders for his execution. There remained the possibility that it had been the reckless act of some young hothead. That seemed the most plausible explanation. It was soon done, in those days.

Omar Douidi the gravedigger was the only one to refute this theory and still to bear Karmoni a grudge.

'It was the people's justice!' he declared.

I should add that Karmoni had never in his life bought Omar a drink.

'What!' Karmoni would exclaim indignantly. 'You're just waiting to bury me, and you expect me to buy you a drink! I'd cut off my hand rather than give you one!'

When the patriots hiding in the mountains saw one of Karmoni's lorries approaching in the distance they danced and clapped for joy.

'*Rezak dja!*' they cried. 'Here comes Rezak!'

Rezak – he who brings all good gifts.

MOHAMMED DIB

The End

Monsieur Albert arrived in great distress. 'They've gone, sir! They've all deserted the farm!'

He even forgot to give the perfunctory military salute with which he always greeted his employer.

Jean Brun understood in a flash – his workmen, too, had gone off to the mountains to join the *others* . . .

'What, all of them?'

'All of them,' echoed the clerk.

Jean Brun was annoyed with himself for having asked. He had been expecting something like this for quite a time. Yet he would never have thought that the news would come as such a shock. He believed he was the exception, that neither he nor his farm would be affected by the troubled times. A deep understanding bound him to these simple folk, his farm labourers; he had friendly feelings towards them and had the impression that they returned the sentiment. Surely he was not mistaken, he couldn't be mistaken. And yet . . .

He did not know what to think, his mind had gone blank; he was transfixed. But only for a moment. Then he pulled himself together. 'Come, come,' he said to himself. 'It's a trust based on years of joint effort. This can't be possible! Years! It's been going on for ages! It's not possible that overnight. . . . Unless all that . . . all that was nothing but lies.' Jean Brun suddenly wanted to laugh at such an absurd idea. But he at once felt a harsh dark wind on his heart, very different from the wind moaning across the fields, which was a herald of spring. The colonist suddenly saw disaster ahead.

He silenced his fears. 'Nothing is lost,' he told himself.

Nothing is lost? guffawed an inner voice that he did not recognize. *Everything is lost!* He thought to himself: 'Here I am getting all nervy and wincing at the first difficulty I meet. I must keep a grip on myself.'

The pale, misty light of morning was spreading over a strange emptiness. Jean Brun scanned the countryside on which winter was only just loosening its grip. As far as the eye could see, the land was all his. Nothing was stirring in all that mist and vastness, nor on the surrounding hills where the grass was tough, the grey rock broke through in patches, and the ravines were rushing torrents. Those spurs dotted with tiny shacks usually came to life very early with the comings and goings of peasants, their donkeys and flocks of goats. But now nothing stirred, as if the heights had been hastily evacuated. Brun's eyes turned back to his own land and his gaze wandered over the silvery olive trees and the rugged brown of the ploughed fields. It was a fine estate, in good heart and all of a piece. A cross-wind ruffled his hair. This unusual stillness and emptiness were unsettling. The very wind carried a vague warning. 'It'll all come right in the end,' Jean Brun said to himself. 'There must be some mis-understanding.' *Fool!* came the other voice. *A misunderstanding? Idiot! You'll see what will happen!* He angrily silenced that voice. 'Nothing will happen! None of what you're imagining! I know what I'm talking about. Just one word from me, and they'll be back at work again.'

He could say, without boasting, that he had been able to win the affection of his workers. He had had no thought for himself when it was a question of the well-being of his employees or their families, and he adopted the native motto, 'Do good, and forget it; you will be repaid'.

Again that derisive laugh broke through his thoughts. 'Yes, I've done a lot of good!' he affirmed. 'I've always been sympathetic towards them. It's nothing more than a misunderstanding!' The venomous laugh continued, gnawing at his heart. *Yet they've refused to come down from their rocky perches this morning. Oh yes, you've been a good friend to them, but they just haven't come!*

You say that you're not ashamed of your feelings, but watch out!

'I should like to know how they'll manage to live without the work I provide for them. What's got into them? How did they reach this point? Obviously!' he thought, and the blood rushed to his head, making him hot in the face. 'No, I shan't give way! I shan't change anything. Change . . . ?' He was surprised at himself for thinking it. A moment later there came another rush of blood, icy this time, opening wide the gates on a countryside given over to desolation. From beyond it all came that inner voice. *We shall give way. We've already given way. But it's too late. Too late!* And the barren expanse vanished, was replaced by this land he owned, with the sap pulsing under his feet and forming a living shield round him.

They would come back. They would work. Jean Brun gazed at his land; it appeared to stretch mute and sombre below the foam of the olive trees. He knew however that it was good and generous, but never before had he seen it with the withdrawn aspect as now. Questingly his eyes roamed over the deep stillness. Everything that had been mastered and tamed had suddenly melted away, it seemed to him; only a strange hostility remained. For some unknown reason, he imagined a woman being held in someone's arms yet who, at the same time, could be seen standing in the far distance, inaccessible. Actually, no words could have expressed what he was thinking; for, complicated though his thoughts were, they all added up to something much simpler and more direct than any everyday expression.

He let a feeling of security seep into him. This land would preserve him from any threat. But, he suddenly realized, the threat came from the land itself! The land contained a threat! Those who did not return to work of their own accord would be forced to it with the whip. And be glad to do it, too! They'll have the whip behind them to their dying day! He remembered what fat old Rémusse had said to him a few months previously at the Colonists' Centre: 'You've got to go the whole hog! And tame them, crush them. It's all or nothing.' And he, Jean Brun, had not agreed, had in fact tried to calm him down, to reason with him. Fool that he was! 'I'm afraid I've made an enemy of him now. He was right, he saw more clearly than I did.'

And now the wind was whispering confidently, bringing words that had long been ready. 'After all, it's a good thing to give them a lesson from time to time, to show them they can't do just what they like.' And once again he caught the echo of Gabriel Rémusse's voice, emphasizing his words: 'To be a friend of the fellahs is to disturb the peace.' In his eyes, that wretched population was like a curse lying on the land.

'If you don't like what we're doing,' the General had said the other day at a reception for the colonists of the region, 'we'll just wash our hands of the whole business. We'll leave you to defend your property and yourselves. But if we're going to protect you, you must help us; and not only help us, but approve of the punitive measures we take. That's a rule there's no getting away from. And in that case, pardon my saying so, we're no worse than you. Let us act sternly and without flinching, and, I repeat, to the best of our ability.'

As he spoke, this man on whom the years had taken their toll had a gentle, pitying look in his eyes, a look marked by a sort of preoccupied disillusionment. And once again he, Jean Brun, was the man who had opposed the repressive measures intended to bring the peasants to order. 'It's only a flash in the pan. Leave it alone, and it will die out. But if you fan it, the whole land will be laid waste. What you propose practically amounts to setting the whole country ablaze.' As he was saying that, he had been struck by his way of expressing himself. How different he was from the other man, the General, even in his way of speaking! He had used short sharp sentences, just as his workmen did. That man didn't know. He didn't know all that could be done with the Arabs through friendliness. He would never understand that. He didn't belong here. It was impossible to argue with men who did not know this country.

Such was the thought in Jean Brun's mind.

And he recalled a group of fellahs that he had come upon one morning, standing round a fire they had lit between three large stones and holding their hands out to it. They had been there some time; it was winter. He had stopped and said, 'Rest in peace!'

'*Salam!*' they replied.

'Is that all you can find to do?' he had said jokingly.

They had made no answer. Their breath was drifting like smoke in the icy air. Standing stock-still, they gazed as though spellbound at the red glow which was throbbing like a big heart among the stones. The glare lit up their faces and was reflected in their eyes for a moment. At that instant an odd feeling of being out of his element took hold of Jean Brun; but simultaneously, as he faced those ragged, bent figures, something gripped at his heart, was held there for ever. And it sang, in the thick, gloomy mist. Jean Brun contemplated the fields extending deep into the distance that wintry morning, and he heard only its voice. It was not hushed even when he stopped looking at his vines, his fields of wheat and his orange groves; and yet his heart was suddenly and unbearably flooded with uncertainty. Throughout the winter, weird and frightening figures of peasants had wandered about like spectres risen from the depths of the land, which stretched stark and silent.

Now the harsh breath of spring was chafing the fields, sweeping them incessantly, and ruffling Jean Brun's hair. A touch of baldness gave him a wide forehead, and below this well-formed brow his faded blue, calm eyes had an obstinate look in them. He was wearing his everyday, light-grey suit, now rather shabby. He was not very tall, of average build, and although over fifty his features still looked remarkably young, especially when the wind had coloured his cheeks, as on that morning. His jacket was flapping open, showing a thin silver chain glittering across his waistcoat. He dismissed his clerk, merely muttering, 'What do they think they're up to?'

He was surprised at his disagreeable tone of voice. He walked back to the farmhouse, a large L-shaped building with a courtyard whose walls were topped with broken glass. Standing out against the lowering sky, the rose-coloured walls and round-tiled roof seemed to be suffusing light. There was the usual activity in the square courtyard; a few workmen were going between the barn and the cowshed, the stables and the drinking-trough, and some domestic servants were bustling in and out. Nothing here indicated that the day was different from any other. Nevertheless, Jean Brun gazed thoughtfully at these men and women. It was as though he was seeing them for the first time, and they appeared out of place here. Why had these stayed? Were they different from the others? Could it be that they were not all alike? Perhaps! They, in any case, were carrying on with their work as though unaware of his presence. And he was reminded of another scene, one at which he had been an unintentional spectator.

The village schoolmaster, a Frenchman, was loading his trunks on to the cart which was to take him to the railway station a couple of miles away. He was believed to have been guilty of subversive talk, and the colonists of the region had demanded that he be recalled. A group of fellahs who had been waiting at the far end of the village approached the schoolmaster. A little surprised, he stopped loading his luggage and, although he did not understand the language, stood ready to listen to them. Looking rather scared, they had pushed an old man towards him. This Arab hesitated for a moment or two, then said in French: 'You must come back.'

He repeated this several times, motioning towards the ground. 'You must come back. You must come back. We are not the people who are sending you away. Don't forget, when you're over there in your own country, that we are waiting for you to come back.'

The Arab looked up at the schoolmaster, who nodded his head. He understood! Tight-lipped, he kept his eyes on the other's tanned, wrinkled old face with its tangled grey beard.

'Don't forget that these men are your brothers!'

The fellah turned towards the others, who were listening trustingly but not saying a word.

'We know that you are a brother to us and that you will come back when our enemies have bowed their heads. . . . So we shall be waiting for you.'

The old man's eyes shone brightly. He added: 'He who teaches his fellow-men spreads the blessing of God.'

He stepped closer, took the schoolmaster's hand and raised it quickly to his lips.

A silence had hovered over the group. The other peasants had drawn away and left the two together.

Jean Brun did not linger in the courtyard but went into the house thinking that he had better check the weapons.

MOHAMMED DIB

Naema - Whereabouts Unknown

Five weeks have gone by, and still no news of Naema. Nothing at all. Some people think she's imprisoned in the Bedeau barracks. The Bedeau barracks . . . the prisoners held there are considered to be hostages; dreadful things are said about what happens to them.

How to be sure? It's impossible to get any definite news, no one has ever returned home from that place. Wait, that's all — for some news to trickle through, for Naema, by some miracle, to be brought to trial. Wait — that's all that's left to us.

I take the children out, often to the public gardens that we call 'the little garden', where we spend a short time in the afternoons. Autumn is tinging the foliage, and its russets and yellows mingle with the blue of the sky. We cannot stay long. Everyone leaves the gardens early in the evening and it is dangerous to linger on. Still, the children enjoy being there. And I, too, find there the only moments of relief that I ever have now. It will happen to all of us, in this war.

But if some do come through safely, they will have learnt a lot. Rahim, who is only seven, has already lived through three years of war, and he looks at me so seriously and with mute questioning that I am upset and feel guilty.

A few days ago I asked him why he was staring at me in that manner.

'You mustn't dawdle, Daddy, must you, when you throw a grenade?' he said.

Sadness overwhelmed me. What could I say to him? Pitch him a tale? That doesn't work any more, not even with Rahim.

Killings, attacks, ambushes . . . there's an echo of it all in his words and thoughts. I don't try to teach him to be careful, for he wouldn't understand. There's already this rent between us.

Another day, all unsuspecting, I laughingly asked him: 'What do you think ought to be done?'

'Kill the lot. Keep throwing bombs.'

He had answered without a moment's hesitation and still gazing at me with his innocent look.

'You'd do that, would you?'

'Yes. Wouldn't you?'

'No,' I said.

I can still see the incredulous look he gave me.

The other tenants rarely mention Naema now. I do my best to be a mother to the children while she's in prison. The women from the other flats do most of the household chores for me, sweeping out, cooking the meals, washing up, doing the laundry. It was they who took over; on no account would they have allowed a man to do such tasks. Sometimes they even give Benali, Zahya and Rahim their meal while I'm away. A veiled woman regularly brings a sum of money – the allowance from the Liberation Front – which they hand over to me. This woman has never shown them her face, and they have never managed to find out who she is. Besides, they take good care not to ask too many questions.

The tenement is in a state of perpetual commotion. It was still dark this morning, a cool and sweet-smelling day was dawning, when raised voices and terrified whisperings ran through the building. Fortunately, it was only a false alarm. These spasms of nervous tension are frequent and reach their highest pitch after bomb-explosions. On those occasions, some of the tenants come hurrying back with news, shout it to the others, and everyone rushes down into the courtyard to add his or her comment. Nothing like that happened this morning, but the day had only just begun.

In the midst of all these upheavals, my thoughts turn

to Naema. Not to know where she is, what they have done to her, is a torment. In the town, disappearances, deaths and funerals have become so numerous that no one counts them any more, and those of today cause yesterday's to be forgotten.

There are posters everywhere showing men being shot. Every day, the courts pass sentences of death. Summary executions increase, and every dawn discloses mutilated corpses. Most of my neighbours think that Naema will not return; they do not dare tell me so, but I can see it on their faces.

Yesterday, two strangers stopped me in the street and made me keep watch outside a tailor's workshop. When they had gone, the tailor said to me in a most natural way, 'Yes, they left some things here.'

'What do you mean?'

'Well!' he said.

I understood.

And it came to me then, that my only reaction to danger now is one of defiance.

This afternoon, as I was crossing the street leading to Soc-el-Ghezel Square, which is always teeming with people, it happened. First, the crowd wavered and fell back, and there were some shrieks. Two shots had just rung out, followed by an explosion. People pushed and trod on one another; in a twinkling, the square emptied. Only the body of a man was left lying there, face down. I made off, in order not to be nabbed by the police, whose whistles were already piercing the air.

I took refuge in a shoemaker's shop in a near-by narrow street.

'Well, what is it? What's going on? Something new?' asked the cobbler, surprised at my hurried entry.

'All that's new is that someone's been killed in Soc-el-Ghezel,' I said, and stopped for breath.

'Ah!' was his only comment.

A smile lit up the pallor of his long, delicate face. 'I'd have wagered it was peace, I'd have wagered that you were bringing peace.'

'Peace?' I said. 'That's something no one's ever heard of.'

That moment and his words still stand out very clearly in my memory. All the more clearly as I had barely finished speaking and was laughing rather nervously at my fright, when two more explosions shook the street. We heard wild yells from close at hand, frenzied shooting broke out and quickly developed into a concentrated hail of fire. Figures suddenly bent double and collapsed before our eyes.

The stuttering of sub-machine-guns drew nearer. I suggested to the cobbler that he should shut his shop door. Without a word he went and bolted it and we both dropped to the floor.

I listened to the din which was now sweeping into the street. I don't remember being afraid. I was calm and collected; just curious to know what would happen next. The seconds passed sluggishly.

Then there came a hammering on the door, as though someone was trying to break it down. The cobbler wanted to open it; he looked inquiringly at me. I signed to him not to move. The blows increased in violence, became more imperative, more furious. Finally the door gave way, and a soldier stepped inside. He didn't look far; grabbing my companion by the scruff of the neck, he dragged him outside. On the threshold, he gave him such a violent blow on the chest with the butt of his gun that the cobbler vomited blood and fell to the ground, where he remained face uppermost. I noticed a loft above my head, climbed up and crouched there. But the soldier did not come back.

I waited, lying there in the gloom amongst the rolls of leather. Through a gap in the floorboards I could make out a stretch of the street. Dusk crept into the shop. I lay still, watching, breathing in the smell of leather, and the minutes went by.

The turmoil had passed on; all that could be heard were dull rumblings in the distance. I got to my feet and brushed myself down. As I went out, past the broken door, I had to step over the cobbler's body. The streets I went through were strangely quiet and deserted.

We are prepared to die, but we have not yet learnt to depart this life. That night, everything was silent – my thoughts, the town, the war. I sat up and looked around; it all seemed so absurd to me. The children were asleep. Why these children? What were they doing there? I had a sudden desire to dress and hurry out to the old town, despite the curfew. It took me a long time to get to sleep again, and when I did my head seemed to be rolling in an ever-mounting tide.

As soon as dawn streaked the sky, I went out. People were already hurrying about their business, cyclists were weaving through the crowds, ringing their bells, and street vendors were cluttering the pavements. In Soc-el-Ghezel Square the only shops still shut were those whose owners had been killed. The walls were scarred by bullets and the shop shutters had jagged tears in them still; I had not dreamt it. Broken glass and splintered brick were strewn about the roadway.

I arrived at the shoemaker's shop.

Shut. I had left it open yesterday. This morning there was a padlock on the street door. I stood there looking at it. What had been done about the shoemaker? I went to see the near-by shopkeepers in the hope of finding out a little more than I already knew. But not a word could I get from them, except that there would be no funeral. All the dead had been collected during the night, taken to the cemetery and buried by the authorities without their relatives being informed.

I walked away and roamed aimlessly about. I felt detached from this clear day. I had to think. But the yawning sky, the balmy air and the flavour of things prevented thought.

I wandered round for a long time. Everything, I soon realized, had the smell and taste of blood.

.   .   .   .   .

It was night again, and again I was snatched from sleep. I listened. Shouts and yells were coming from houses in the distance. Then more uproars, just as fearful, spread from place to place. Shots were whipping through the air, broken by bursts from sub-machine-guns. I lay still, holding my breath. The cries of pain and terror were coming from men and women. Then silence fell. I closed my eyes. The beasts of the Apocalypse were roaming the land.

Only the distant purring of motors could be heard; then that, too, faded away.

Morning came. A light-blue sky and a dazzling light. And there was no one who did not leave home without a pang of impatience in his heart.

Mutilated bodies have been found, dropped at the gates of the town. A dozen, three of them women.

The war goes on; it may last for years yet. No one can now imagine what life is like without continual bursts of firing and explosions. News of horrible things is whispered around. I hardly ever walk along the streets without often glancing back, without being ready to throw myself flat if a grenade is thrown or a bomb goes off. The glimpse of any suspicious gesture puts me on my guard; I never wait to see what might happen. Once you leave home, you cannot be sure of returning alive.

There are some squares and market-places and intersections, especially those patrolled by the Riot Squad, that I always avoid now, as I do streets and alleys with barbed-wire barriers. It's not wise to take refuge in one of them when an outrage occurs; you find yourself caught in a trap.

While we remain at the mercy of these butchers, bound hand and foot, the real war is taking place elsewhere. So we find our only defence against this daily terror is in disturbances and the breakdown of law and order. We have paid too dearly already, to hesitate or draw back. Something has got under way which is even worse than war.

There are times when I should like to meet my death in one of the numerous outrages committed every day; this blood that splashes us, this stench as from a slaughter-house, makes me heave and fills me with horror. Then I suddenly feel such a hunger for life, such a thirst to know what it will all be like *after*, that I am ready to face all the armies and police forces in the world.

How will those who survive the war adapt themselves to life? What will the return to peace mean to them? For us, the world has lost its savour and its colour. How will they manage to give it a human face again?

I had no sooner sat down at the Tizaoui café, a short time ago, than a patrol descended on us; and with all the other customers at the terrace tables I was pushed inside with my hands above my head. We stood packed tightly together, each waiting his turn to be searched and have his identity checked. The black muzzles of automatic weapons promised death to anyone foolish enough to move. We stood without flinching and in silence, a silence over which a strange calm reigned. I said to myself, 'They won't, they won't get the better of us.'

The checking lasted an hour, an hour in which each man had to put his self-control to the test. Then we were released into an afternoon laden with menace. My throat was sore from the insults I had swallowed. Curfew, which was at half-past four, would soon be emptying the streets. I left the café, but instead of going straight home I decided to walk round for a bit. The fronts of houses were set in deathly expectation. People were going about in silence, walking carefully. The town was hunched up in itself and had its look of evil days.

At the end of the boulevard the blue Mansourah hills were standing out against a pale sky, and cast an unfailing promise of happiness into my face. I would have walked round the ramparts, gone through the gates and . . . If it had still been possible!

The aim of my stroll was merely the newspaper-kiosk in the Place de l'Hôtel de Ville; as I knew the paper-seller slightly I should be able to glance at all the papers without being obliged to buy any. I read the news, which was much like the previous day's, and went on my way again. I was walking past the museum railings and had just reached the corner, when it happened. The blast shook the walls around me so violently that I was brought up against a rush of air, which scorched my face. At the same moment, there came a deafening avalanche of glass and cries rose from all sides. People were scattering in every direction across the tree-lined square. I plunged down the nearest street. That, too, was noisy with cries, shouts, orders.

A burst of small-arms fire swept the street. A man fell just in front of me, and then a woman, who got entangled in her long veil.

The street froze.

Sirens wailing loudly, some army trucks arrived, braked violently, and armed paratroops swarmed down. One of them, with icy blue eyes, motioned that I could go. I made off. But at the corner of the next street some Arab Territorials shouted to me to stop.

I halted. Then, looking straight at them, I made the decision to walk towards them. At every moment I expected them to open fire on me. I was quite cool and calm, and filled with disdain. 'They shan't have the satisfaction of seeing the man they shoot cringe before them,' I was thinking as I forced myself to go forward. Among them were some whose faces I knew by sight; a few had been at school with me.

'Don't move!' shouted one of the group.

I took a few more steps, then a sick feeling came over me. I don't remember just what happened after that. I was led back to the square, having received a blow on the back of the neck. I found myself standing with a number of other Algerian Arabs being held at gun-point. There were dead and dying bodies sprawled in the roadway. Just in front of us one of the dying was moaning feebly, 'Help me, help . . .'

No one made the slightest move to go to his aid. In the square and the streets leading off it, the man-hunt was continuing. Uniformed figures, bent forward over their pointed weapons, were chasing other running figures. One or the other of these would suddenly throw up his arms and fall forward, to merge with the grey of the ground.

Just then, a man coming out of a bar spotted someone in a corner and started to gesticulate and shout. 'That's him! That's the man who left the bomb! I saw him do it!'

The other looked at him in bewilderment and clutched a rubbishy basket to his shabby black jacket. A few of the Territorials ran across and grasped him by the arms. The man made no resistance. They dragged him to the middle of the square, then shot him several times in the chest and stomach. He sank to the ground, still clutching his worthless basket.

The man who had denounced him, a bookseller, shouted, 'Hurrah for justice!'

It was undoubtedly he, that poor little man, who saved us all; a builder's labourer by the look of him, smaller still in death, lying there in the middle of the square, rigid, but seeming to challenge the whole world now. I could not tear my eyes away from him or rid my mind of his muteness.

Soon afterwards, in fact, we were allowed to go. The military cordons were withdrawn, and people again moved about freely; cyclists darted along, customers went into shops and others came out, a rag-and-bone man uttered his plaintive cry and a streettrader came along pushing his barrow. The fright was over. Only a faint smell of blood still lingered, but it lay over everything, weighing down heart and mind. I went on my way, up the street that led back home.

There is still the same suspense, the same lunacy. Still the same gaping abyss which engulfs our lives.

This morning, twenty bodies were found laid out on the square in the old town. I hurried there, as did lots of other people; faces with burning eyes were staring out of windows.

Soldiers were holding back the crowds from the approaches to the square and erecting barriers at all the entrances. It was impossible to go any farther. I dodged from one place to another.

Suddenly there appeared the most astounding procession ever seen in the town. It consisted entirely of children and Arab women without their veils, and this impulsive torrent was sweeping forward shrieking out the Liberation Anthem. Violence, rage, suffering or defiance. It was impossible to tell which was the dominant force driving these women and barefoot children towards the machine-gun carriers. A white and green flag made from old clothing and tied to a stick fluttered above their heads. The paratroops formed up round the square, and as the women went past they knocked off their berets.

All at once, automatic weapons began to stutter. Everything swam before my eyes. And we others, we who were watching them, listening to their harsh voices rising to the sky, we seemed to merge into the same melting-pot of blood and death. I wanted to run across to them, to bellow that anthem with them and be exposed to that fire.

The hail of bullets was turned on us. Everyone scattered, trampled on others amid cries and screams, dropped to their knees.

Two o'clock in the morning.

An explosion shatters the silence. A rumbling can be heard in the distance. Then the darkness is punctuated by shots, which provoke spasmodic bursts of firing. Half-tracks shake the houses as they clatter past. And that is all. Nothing more is heard. The silence makes another wall in the night.

Dawn rises in creamy freshness, and oceans of light pour forth; even the cicadas are affected by it and break into song. Children swarm out of the houses and take over the street.

A wild hope buoys me up today. Does it spring from a desire to survive the general collapse, in spite of everything? I'm ready to swear, believe it or not, that tomorrow will bring safety, peace and victory! I draw myself up, radiating strength, and I hold out – no, give – courage to others.

Nevertheless, refugees are beginning to flock in from the countryside. Hungry and exhausted, they bring the smell of the earth with them, a breath of dread and a speechless violence. I think of the peace of the fields around the town, and of the menace concealed in that peace. Even the trees, quite still, their fawn foliage licked by unseen flames, seem on the watch for something.

But seeing the women at their doors or gathered in the courtyard, hearing their voluble chatter, gives me the peculiar impression that nothing has changed, that nothing will ever change. Like this continuous lovely weather. Neither fog not rain will ever spoil it. What sheer folly it is, this weather!

I am still at liberty and still alive, but every day I wonder what I have done to deserve this and what good it is. There are constant bursts of firing, my thoughts go immediately to Naema, then revert to the dangers that every moment brings. I think of her at night, when I lie awake staring into the darkness and listening to the slightest noise in the town, but especially when morning comes and the children wake up, and we have most need of her presence. These bright, blue mornings, almost like winter mornings, are what would most likely reconcile me to the world were it not that I get up as I had gone to bed – with anguish lodged in my heart.

Life is a benumbing nightmare, although this waiting slowly brings acceptance of the inevitable. I am gradually beginning to think that I shall never see Naema again, that she will not come back, will never walk about this room again. However, I go on living, I still listen for the sounds and voices in the building and lend an ear to the tales of the neighbours.

We have had several very windy days. The glories of autumn were swept away and grey weather at last set in. The trees braced themselves, while above their withered branches dark clouds crowded the sky. Even in my despair and indifference, I was glad of this change. The last days of autumn had become unbearable, with all their brilliance, light and purity.

Then it started to rain – a real deliverance. The rain continued

D

for a long time, incessant, pervading, stifling, sliding slowly over the dried-up land. Street warfare was in abeyance.

As I turn the pages of this diary, it is still raining, seems never to have stopped raining since that time. I wasted still more days and weeks going round the sodden, streaming town making inquiries, begging for news, knocking at innumerable doors in my efforts to find my wife. It was yesterday, but it seems like today. All was in vain. The rain is still falling from a murky sky on bare trees and houses darkened by the wet. I look out at this lowering sky, the same overcast sky as then, and the same steamy, misty streets, the same passing phantoms appear before my eyes. I was then still sustained by some kind of hope, but hope so enclosed in inaccessible places that I now hesitate to call it hope. A stone had been dropped into an abyss and I listened to its interminable fall. I was that stone, and the hope I clung to was that it would never reach the bottom.

From time to time, when a bright interval cast a dull light over the town, I would go out and wander about the streets. I tried to take an interest in other people's lives, for want of interest in my own; in this way, I didn't think about myself. Then one morning, quite early, someone came to the tenement and asked to see me.

I knew the man waiting at the door only slightly. He drew me aside, then began talking in a low voice. He explained that since the death of a certain shoemaker, they had been in some difficulty; his shop was in a very useful position and its role had not been discovered by the police, in spite of what had happened. So it could be used again.

'You must have been a friend of his,' the man added, 'as you went to ask his neighbours what had become of him, the morning after the massacre. Since then, we haven't been able to find anyone to replace him and open up the shop. Especially someone who's known in the neighbourhood. And it's absolutely essential to make use of those premises again. Perhaps you would like to. . . . Oh, you've time to think it over, we won't hurry you! You needn't give an answer at all, if you don't care to.'

I let him deliver his little speech, giving me time to sum him up.
'Have you the keys?' I said when he had finished.

He produced a ring with two keys from his trouser pocket. I took it, and he went off.

I am closing this diary now. It was thinking of my wife, the shoemaker and the others, which sustained me and helped me to carry on until now. They knew why they died, they did.

DRISS CHRAIBI

Four Trunks

Coulibaly landed at Bordeaux one morning in November. He was, to be exact, the last to go ashore, after all the passengers, after all the people who had come aboard to meet passengers (*will he come too*, Coulibaly wondered, *will my brother come to meet me?*), after all manner of important people in uniform or livery, even after the captain of the ship whom he stopped to greet and thank – the voyage had been smooth, the food plentiful, the service perfect except over the matter of the trunks; and he, Coulibaly Bingo, veterinary surgeon in the lion country, would be glad for the captain to convey to the Admiral of the Shipping Line and to the Company Director his most sincere thanks and his kindest regards.

Although the captain wore much gold braid, and tried in vain to compose his features in an expression of grave authority proper to the wearing of much gold braid, when faced with this tall devil of a fellow in a crumpled suit but graver than himself and who flourished his arms wildly while speaking, he could not help laughing. But it was only an inner laugh. Just his eyes, for a brief moment, showed his merriment. For he realized that if he laughed openly in front of this person who during the whole voyage had created such a commotion over God alone knew what trunks, then he would remain on board for ever. *And I too might have been just such a child*, he thought. *For that's what he is, with a child's illusions, the dreams and all the credulity of a child. And to think that there are people who come back from this child's country with a low fever or a liver complaint!*

He gave him what he believed was a firm handshake – but which was really a renunciation. For a moment he had established

DRISS CHRAIBI Four Trunks

a kind of bridge between his present self and the child he had been so long ago – but he was immediately recalled by his responsibilities, by duty and life itself. And to Coulibaly, that handshake brought disillusion. The first.

'Right!' the captain said to him. 'I'll convey your thanks to the admiral and the company director. And now will you kindly go ashore.'

'I can't. My trunks are still on board.'

'If you don't go ashore, you'll never get them.'

'Really?'

'That's how it is. Regulations, you know. Good-bye!'

So Coulibaly went down the gangway. When he had come to the conclusion that, everything considered, this captain was a sensible man and that he could depend on his advice just as he had trusted him during the voyage, he went down the gangway. *I've never had any misgivings, and that's what amazes me. Now I mistrust everything and everybody. Why?*

And he stood there at the foot of the gangway, as still as a rock, smiling, willing. He was waiting for his trunks. His four trunks.

Because I really do have misgivings, he was thinking. *For although this captain has been capable of transporting me across miles and miles of ocean and bringing me safe and sound to port, in this case to Bordeaux, there's nothing to show that, at the same time, he's attended to details, in this case to my trunks – and that I'll find them safe and sound again. Perhaps it was his handshake just now. Perhaps it's me feeling lost and bewildered already. Or homesick already.*

Around him were great cranes grunting and groaning as they worked, and ships come from distant horizons calling to each other by blowing their sirens, and a never-ending bustle of faces and feet and voices. Standing there in the midst of it all, he kept wondering where his brother could emerge from and where the sun could emerge from, and whether the two would emerge at the same time into this greyness filled with factory noises, and whether they would ever emerge.

When he had gathered that sooner or later men would take away the gangway whose side he was clutching with both hands (and clinging to with all his force), when he had ventured into the world of faces, feet, and voices which frightened him (though he was still smiling, for he knew how to approach a band of lions), and when he entered the customs shed he continued to have misgivings and to wonder why, and what they signified. The customs officer thought the smile was for him, and his bad temper vanished at once. The four trunks were piled one on top of the other, and he stood in front of them – rigid as a statue come down from its pedestal.

The customs officer did not say 'Couldn't you have got here quicker, you black idiot? Don't think I'm going to work over-time because of you, cock. That may be the way of it where you come from, but you're in a civilized country now. And what are you grinning away like an ape for? You're beginning to get on my nerves.' The customs officer said none of that, but he thought it all the same. He said to him, 'These trunks yours?'

And because he was what he called 'a decent old sod', and because the Negro went on smiling, he added with just a touch of severity, '. . . sir?'

'The captain did attend to details too,' said Coulibaly in a triumphant voice. 'He fully deserves his gold bands.'

'What captain's this? I asked you if these are your trunks, are they or aren't they?'

'You see,' the other began to explain evenly, 'it's been one long trouble over these trunks. I'd stacked them in my cabin —'

'That'll do!' exclaimed the customs officer. 'Open them!'

Coulibaly was quite unperturbed. He knew that you must act calmly where lions are concerned, so as not to excite them. Therefore he went on more evenly, carefully separating each syllable.

'The steward came and told me that the ship was neither an old tramp nor a fishing vessel, but a passenger-liner, a liner of a big Company, which had a special hold for the passengers' luggage, and that in no circumstances was the luggage badly treated, not even trunks. "Rats?" the steward said, "What rats? I've told you, you've got the Company's cover, signed and receipted, for yourself and your luggage." I said to the steward – I pointed out to him most politely that these trunks —'

'And I'm telling you to open them,' the customs officer shouted in a high-pitched voice. 'Open your precious trunks and let's get finished.'

He sent them toppling to the ground with a sudden sweeping drop of his arm, and was ready to kick them open himself, then to get them out of the customs shed with more kicks. There was a limit to everything, even to the patience of a decent old sod. Coulibaly remained unperturbed. He closed his fists, sniffed at them shortly one after the other – and, when he thrust them forward, rubbed them vigorously together under the customs officer's nose, as though they were two stones for sparking a light. For he was aware that some lions do not respond to kindly treatment, and stronger measures are necessary in their case.

'If it's my trunks you're talking about,' he said in a clear voice, 'then they're indeed precious! They're so precious that I've been watching over them since leaving Korhogho on the Ivory Coast. But there's no need to shout it or even to whisper it. I know already. I'm perfectly well aware of it, I'm telling you. And it's because I'm aware of it that I make so much trouble.'

'Stop!' the customs officer cried, exasperated. 'I haven't the faintest idea what you're gabbling about.'

'Of course not! If you go about yelling in the wind, you don't hear the wind. And I'm not gabbling. I'm speaking French. I've my diplomas – I'm a veterinary surgeon from the lion country.'

'All right then,' decided the other, even more exasperated. 'You're speaking French, and I don't hear the wind because I'm yelling. But listen to me. One of us is going crazy, if he isn't already.'

Coulibaly gave a wide smile. 'Please God,' he said, 'let it be me.'

The customs officer stared hard at him for a moment. He was

ready to give a swipe like a woodcutter or to burst into tears. He
did not know what was happening to him. But he was convinced
that the more he argued with this Negro the more ridiculous he
would become. He closed his eyes in silent prayer and called on
the regulations for aid, all the sanctions and battery of precisely-
worded rules which could sweep away any tricky situation and
which had always protected him like a suit of armour. For he
knew that left to himself he was just a decent old sod – one of
those tough guys, as his wife said, who are always talking of
smashing someone's face in but have never hurt a fly.

When he opened his eyes again, the Negro was still there; and
this seemed to astonish him.

'Listen,' he said. 'I don't want any trouble, all I want is to go
and have my supper. So will you let me get on?'

Coulibaly rubbed his hands together as though washing them.
His smile stretched from ear to ear.

'I knew I wasn't dreaming,' he said. 'All I was hoping for was
just a little human warmth. That's why I made so much fuss on
board. But neither the steward nor the captain realized.'

'Now please,' the other protested. 'Don't let's start all over
again.'

Coulibaly's smile vanished. 'For God's sake,' he said, 'what's
the matter with all these people who've no time to spare, who
know what you're going to say before you open your mouth, and
don't want to listen to anything?'

He, too, closed his eyes, but opened them again almost at once.
During that short moment he had not called on any one nor
anything.

'It's years since I took a holiday,' he added sadly. 'And now
I've got five months. I've saved them up, as others save up coins.
With the wild idea of one day coming and shaking you by the
hand, d'you see?'

'This is the first time you've been to France?'

'D'you see why I saved up five months' holiday?'

'Yes, I do,' said the customs officer. 'I swear that I see very
clearly now.'

He suddenly felt very awkward, and was surprised to find his mouth had gone dry.

'Listen,' he went on. 'Don't take offence at this, but – I'm asking you offhand like – well, what I mean is: you've made me late, and my wife's expecting me home for supper. To punish you, would you like to come and have supper with us? It'll be pot-luck, you know.'

Coulibaly said nothing. He just nodded his head several times, with increasing energy.

'It'll be so that you can get your own back,' the customs officer explained. 'You can invite me when I go to your country.'

He did not add: 'But I know I never shall. For years I've been saving up too, to buy a house on mortgage not too far from Paris, to grow cabbages and leeks, and go fishing. God and I alone know what it costs to retire like that. Listen – when I say I'll go to your country, it's just a manner of speaking, alas.' He said none of that, but thought it all the same, with a kind of calm hopelessness. He thought, too, of an old gun that was going rusty somewhere up in the attic, and of all the lions he had resolved, when a boy, to shoot down. He made no mention of that either. He just kept puffing out his cheeks, faster each time. And when he did speak it was in a booming voice.

'But I must remind you,' he said, 'that I'm first and foremost a customs official.'

Coulibaly nodded once again. He loosened his tie and unfastened his collar. The bunch of keys dangling from his neck jingled gaily. He did not undo them, but squatted down holding the bunch in the hollow of his hand like an amulet. One key after another, he turned them in a dozen or so locks and padlocks, and slowly unfastened the straps. Then he knelt right down and opened the trunks. They were empty.

And it came about, one morning, that Simone had just hung up her coat in the cloakroom and had sat down on her tall stool, between her typewriter and the switchboard; she was half-way between sitting and standing when he entered the office – or, to be exact, when he began to enter. All these little details she was to remember later, with pitiless clarity, on a night of thunderstorms and gales while watching Joseph sleeping, naked in her arms.

When Coulibaly began to come in she really thought she was going to die, for try as she would to laugh, she was beyond laughing. All she could manage to do, as she dropped astride her stool, was to grasp her typewriter with both hands and lift it, trying to break it into small pieces. A hat crammed down over a forehead, and below the hat two white eyes and thirty-two white teeth – that was what she saw at first, in a flash; the eyes were grave and the smile timid. Then the head vanished and a forefinger appeared. Just a forefinger. This slowly bent and knocked three times, one short and two long, on the side of the lock.

Simone counted up to ten, then to fifteen, and called, 'Come in'.

Once again she saw the hat, the eyes and the teeth. The hat seemed crammed down lower, the eyes seemed graver and the smile more timid, almost scared. But Coulibaly still did not come in. He said, 'Excuse me'.

'That's all right,' Simone replied.

'No – I ought to have rung. But where's the bell?'

Simone raised the typewriter a little higher and again counted up to ten, then to fifteen, and said, 'There isn't one. There's a notice on the door that says "Walk straight in".'

'Oh, is there? I didn't see it. The landing's not well lit. I'm sorry.'

All this while, Simone had seen just the visitor's head peering between the double doors, half-way up, and seeming to her to be hanging there like a hunting trophy. And all this while too, she was still trying to summon laughter to her aid, convinced that when this person came right in she would have hysterics. But still Coulibaly did not come in. Again he said 'Excuse me', and his trunks appeared one after the other, sliding across the polished floor as though on rollers.

Then Coulibaly raised his hat, put it back on his head, and
entered the office. First he attended to his trunks; perceiving an
empty space between the settee and the counter, and gauging it
with half-closed eyes, he then moved the settee, stacked the
trunks, stepped back a couple of paces and, his head held to one
side, gazed admiringly at his efforts for some time. After due
consideration, he patted the top trunk and then slid the flat of his
hand over the whole pile, up and down several times, as if it were
a wall being plastered and his hand a trowel. And there he stood,
rubbing his hands faster and faster. Then he proceeded to attend
to his clothes. That is, he took off his hat and placed it on the
settee, took off his overcoat and jacket and placed these too on
the settee, but at the other end from his hat. His movements were
calculated, as if he were helping a cow to calve. Which is just
what he was repeating, what he was soothingly thinking. He told
himself above all that there was no need to be scared, that he was
a veterinary in the lion country and, after all, lions were as good
as men, be they White, be they wives or daughters of White men.
Just as composedly, he prepared to take off his pullovers. Three
pullovers made of good coarse wool, all of the same pattern, size,
and shade. He rolled them into a bundle which he solemnly
placed on the settee, behind his hat. When he had put on his
jacket and overcoat again he was no longer scared. Conventions
were worth what people believed, and every country had its own.
Why should he be scared? Now he was presentable and could
turn round, talk and smile. But first he arranged his tie, and then
he turned. And when he faced her, Simone knew she was
not going to have hysterics and that she could even raise a
smile.

When he said, 'My name is Coulibaly Bingo, and I've come
from Korhogho to see my brother Joseph, the journalist,' she
stared at her typewriter in bewilderment, wondering when and
why she had picked it up and how she had managed to hold it
there for so long. She put it down slowly, and replied:

'He isn't here. But if you'd care to wait . . .'

And she realized that now she was smiling. And she knew it

was a tight smile. And that in the weeks ahead she would have this same smile on her lips, getting tighter all the time.

And now?

Now that days have gone by, that weeks and months have passed, what can she possibly say to him, what can she reply, what can she think up? Oh, it's not that he asks questions. He never questions. He merely arrives at the same time every morning, as soon as the office opens, brings in his trunks and stacks them in the same place, then sits down on the same settee, in the same position, sits there throughout every working day, upright, dignified, always with a smile – and it's impossible for her not to notice him, not to be aware of the odour, colour, and force of this tragic patience.

The office-cleaner who arrived before dawn and left at daylight never set eyes on him; but she knew of him, knew who he was and why he had come from afar. So did all the people of the neighbourhood, the shopkeepers and paper-sellers, road-sweepers, café regulars, and prostitutes; everyone around knew of him. None had ever spoken to him, yet they all knew of him; he arrived early in the morning and left at nightfall. He was ignored even by the firm's employees, reporters, Press photographers, and hangers-on. When you opened the outer door he was the first person you saw, sitting next to his trunks. But he was almost as rigid as they were, and you quickly perceived that behind his polite manner, behind his look and his smile, was something so much more intense that nothing could express it, something weighty lying there inert. Which was why you hurried on and went through other doors leading to the bustle of work and familiar things, and looked for something to do, sought someone to talk and laugh with. Where, O Lord, could that strange uneasiness come from?

But Simone was unable to do as the others did when they came into the office, hardly pausing before continuing on their way. She knew she was but a minor employee in charge of Inquiries ('Have you an appointment?' – 'What name, please?' – 'Hold the

line, please, I'll find out.' – 'He's in conference.') just as she knew
that the counter formed the boundary of her activities and also
bounded her in – and that she had to remain eight hours a
day opposite this Negro who was waiting. When the telephone
rang, it was a short reprieve. When she had letters to type,
she made dozens of copies. And there were of course people
who came to make inquiries, but she could hardly keep them
there all day, there in front of her, between herself and the
Negro.

Before (because it was *before*), she had brought her lunch with
her, sandwiches and some fruit. The building had been converted,
and what had perhaps been the kitchen was now a 'laboratory'
where agency photos were classified and filed away in the cupboards. There was no gas-ring, not even a water-tap. She used to
eat her sandwiches and fruit seated on the counter, and then go
down to 'Jojo's' café and have a cup or two of coffee. But since
the arrival of the Negro she preferred going to have lunch
in the café. Because he never had lunch. Sitting stock-still as he
did, always quite still, and smiling, always smiling, motionless as
a rock or a dead bird, she was convinced he lived on air, fed on
dreams and patience. In the small scared voice of a child, she told
him not to open the door if anyone knocked, not to answer the
telephone if it rang, and then she closed the door behind her with
a rapidity that always surprised her. Dear God, let him be gone
when I get back; but I know he'll never go!

'Jojo' had soldiered in some part of Africa, but just where he
could not have said. In Africa, the Negroes are all alike to those
people who have perhaps never *seen* them. He would tell that
he'd been a captain, that he'd been all over Africa and had licked
the niggers into shape with the whip and the toe of his boot.
From his stay there he had brought back a copper hammer and
two strict principles: that everyone should call him 'Jojo' (even
his wife, even his children), and never to be behind his bar. He
had gold teeth, was sparing of words, and walked like a strong
man with his arms held wide apart. And it invariably happened
that when he was alone, quite alone, faced with himself, he still

always remembered his time in Africa. Then he bashed at anything or anybody.

When Simone told him of the Negro being in her office for weeks and that his brother the journalist was hiding to avoid seeing him, that she didn't know what to say to this man who was waiting and that she pitied him as she had never pitied a white man or an animal, and that her heart bled for him ever since he'd arrived, she did not know why she was saying all that to a man she'd never spoken to before, and she said it without thinking – but she was ready to do anything, sell or give her body, to see the last of this Negro smiling with a smile which was assuredly a long sob. And while she went on talking, Jojo listened in silence. But when she stopped, his lips curled back in a soundless sneer and he dashed up to the office to break the nigger in four, he shouted as he ran. She hurried after him and found them there, one leaning against the counter and the other on the settee. Both were smiling, and somewhere in the room a bluebottle or mosquito was buzzing about like an aeroplane.

Coulibaly was the first to speak, still smiling. He said, 'I'll show you my trunks, sir.'

'Trunks or not, show or don't show, what are you doing here?' retorted Jojo.

'I'll show you my trunks, sir,' the Negro repeated.

The other began to bawl with all his might. He'd been to Africa and knew the niggers.

'I know you,' he yelled. 'I know you and your kind! Pick up your trunks and bugger off. I've tamed tougher guys than you. Go on, sling your hook!'

'You haven't seen my trunks, sir,' said the Negro. 'I'll show them to you.'

He was getting up as Jojo leapt at him, seemingly shot forward by the counter. There came a flash of gold teeth and the sound of two blows, short and hard. Then Jojo turned towards the door, arms held wide apart and back bent. But he did not know this Negro. When he reached the door, the trunks were there, tossed over his head just like rubber balls. And behind the trunks, as though he were a fifth rubber ball, was the Negro bloody and smiling, repeating with the same sad calmness: 'I'll show you my trunks, sir.'

And he opened them, and said: 'I came to fill them with ideals, sir, here in the capital of ideals, sir, for my brothers of my race and for myself, all the way from Korhogho. And, sir, if you don't know what ideals are, let others believe in them, or at least dream of them. And even you, you're part of an ideal for me, for me and my brothers of my race. And you're the first to give us something of an ideal, so thank you, sir. You have given us blood.'

Calmly, slowly, he spattered the insides of the trunks with his blood.

And that evening Jojo bashed someone again. He shut himself in the bathroom, taking the copper hammer he had brought back from Africa. He had a long look at himself in the mirror and then hit his forehead with the hammer, right between the eyes, with all his might.

Coulibaly spent the last week of his holidays with Simone, in her small attic room.

There was no electricity. They bought three or four bundles of candles and lit them all; then, sitting on the trunks, for seven nights they talked about lions. Neither of them remembered whether they ate or drank anything. Exaltation nourished them as no wine in the whole world could have done. During the entire week they did not sleep.

By day, they were at the newspaper office. They arrived together and left together. Neither the director nor the caretaker dared to say the slightest thing to them – nor even to smile. Whether they were going upstairs or down, or sitting either side of the counter, she on her office stool and he on the settee, they went on looking at each other with the same smile and nourished by the same exaltation – and it was as though they were going on talking aloud about lions.

If someone came along with an inquiry, if one of the regular

callers looked in, or a man full of his own importance went by –
Coulibaly and Simone, without a word to each other, compared
them with lions and burst out laughing. There were letters to
type, which she typed at great speed, sending whirling round her
not the clacking of keys on the roller but the noise of surf pluck-
ing at shingle; the telephone kept ringing and she answered it,
hung up, lifted the receiver again, convinced that the instrument
was a living being with a thousand voices, a thousand faces, and
a thousand souls. While from the ground floor rose the hubbub
of the presses sounding like the sea when the door was closed,
and when the door opened it was like the whole tumult of the sea
rising, with its deep under-swell and its seagulls and its great
waves pounding on the rocks.

'Yes,' said Simone. 'But why the pullovers? Why three
pullovers?'

It was on the last night, by the light of the stumps of the last
candles. In fact, it was the dawn, and perhaps the end of a dream.
Joseph, she thought, *Joseph the journalist. We'll have to talk about
him now. What was the reporting job he went off on, what was the lie,
and the excuse? We've talked about lions and now we're going to talk
about a man.*

Coulibaly explained that Korhogho was on the Ivory Coast
and that Paris was in France.

'That's all,' he added.

Simone looked at him solemnly, then nodded as though she
had understood.

'And the trunks?' she asked. 'I take it you're neither a joker
nor a lunatic.'

'The trunks?' said Coulibaly. 'Oh yes, the trunks . . .'

He went and sat beside her, and told her a long story. There
was once a Negro, the son of a Negro and a Negress. His name
was Coulibaly and he had a brother Joseph. Both attended the
White Man's school, learnt to read and write, to count, to talk and
hink in the language of the White Man. That took years. Then
each was given a diploma on which the Minister of Education
certified, and put his signature and seal in testimony thereof, that

one and the other had passed their exams – as good as saying they were equipped to find a place for themselves in the world, and to hold their own, thanks to this diploma. But it was more than likely that the Minister of Education did not know the Negroes. In any case, Coulibaly and Joseph weighed up their diplomas for a long time and then decided, after mature consideration, to go and find out what was the *real* value of these pieces of paper; and, at the same time, to make acquaintance with the words which were written in books and which were singing in their hearts. To be exact, only one of them was to go; the other would stay behind at Korhogho to work and keep the family. 'And that's what we did, my brother and I,' Coulibaly continued. 'That's to say, we drew straws and I won. But he was the elder, and it was he who went off to the country of ideals, I mean to France, anyway to the country that provided the education and where the Minister for this education lived.

'You see,' he explained, 'words only take on their full importance when confronted with living realities. Don't you agree?'

Simone replied that she agreed entirely.

'But do you see,' he insisted, 'that for a Negro like me the words written in books, words about ideals, about goodness, love, justice and fraternity, for years meant human beings as living as you are, sitting there by my side, who I'm able to touch, to see and feel?'

She said: 'You don't believe in them any more?'

'I'll explain,' he said.

So the Negro and his brother drew straws and the elder went off, charged with the duty of writing regularly to the one left behind and sending him all available information concerning the words written in books, since the elder was going to Paris, capital of ideals, fraternity, and all the other words. And he did in fact write. Nearly every month. And what he wrote was tremendous, not with words but with shafts of light.

'Yes,' said Coulibaly. 'He was a lucky man to be in the capital of ideals, but he was the elder. And I worked away all that time, and I said to myself that I quite understood him, since he never

E

mentioned coming back home. And I told the lions that for all
their strength the whole lot between them, African lions and the
rest, could never have this little shaft of light that sang in my
heart, this ever so little shaft of light which my brother Joseph
sent me every month. And then one day I said to myself:
"Coulibaly, you black idiot, and why shouldn't you?" I reasoned
with myself like this: "Coulibaly, you black idiot, you're a good
Negro and you're supporting the family, but Joseph is better off
than you are, even though he never sends anything to help with
the family. You went to the White Man's school, but I find that
you don't know how to reckon up or how to reason. And from
now on, you're going to, starting this very minute, d'you
understand?" And I understood perfectly. When I had any
money left over, I carefully saved it up. And when I'd two or
three weeks' holiday, I saved them up, too. That's how I came
to land at Bordeaux one fine day with four trunks to fill with
ideals, and I had plenty of time to fill them; five whole months.
And now that my holiday's over, I ask you – where is he? Do
two angels in Paradise shun each other?'

This is the end, she thought, *really the end.*

'Joseph, you mean?' she said.

'Yes, Joseph. My brother. Could it be that he's become a soul
in torment in this paradise?'

'No,' she said slowly. 'It's my turn to explain to you now.'

She did not tell him: 'His eyes have gone yellow through
drinking absinthe, he writes stuff for a Black Men's paper that no
Black Man ever reads, and he spends all his time running after
women.' She did not tell him: 'Nothing remains of the Negro he
was but his rounded back, his accent and his skin.' She did not
tell him: 'You're not just simple, you're credulity itself.'

She told him: 'He's a prominent political journalist and he's
got a great, great deal of work to do, you can take my word for it.
There's a time for dreaming about words, just as there is for
telling stories about lions. There's a time for action too, among
the realities of life and men. Your brother is fully engaged in
those realities. As a political journalist he's leading the fight to

obtain a worthy status for men of his race. You can be proud of him, believe me.'

'I do believe you,' he said. 'I haven't come for nothing. If he's what you say, no, I haven't come for nothing.'

It was only later that she wept, very much later, on a night of thunderstorms and gales. And when she had finished weeping she looked at Joseph, sleeping peacefully and naked in her arms. Her sobbing had not wakened him, and it seemed that nothing, ever, could wake him. 'Poor Joseph!' she said aloud. 'You'll never know that it wasn't to please you that I lied to your brother the morning he left, as I'd lied to him during those five months he was waiting for you in my office. Sleep away, poor Joseph, sleep away! You'll never know either that I gave myself to you tonight in remembrance of your brother, Coulibaly.'

'What's that?' cried Joseph, waking with a start. 'Is Coulibaly here?'

'Go to sleep,' she said. 'You know very well that he went off ten days ago. There's nothing to be afraid of. Go to sleep.'

'Yes, of course. . . . But why aren't you sleeping? What are you doing, sitting up and looking at the candle burning?'

'Me?' she replied. 'Oh, nothing. Nothing much. I'm dreaming about lions.'

The customs officer was at his post. When he saw Coulibaly he started puffing out his cheeks as if playing the bagpipes.

'What did you think of the soup?' he asked.

'First-rate,' said Coulibaly. 'How's it made?'

'With leeks,' the customs officer replied, 'and carrots, turnips, potatoes, a clove of garlic and an onion, let it simmer for half an hour, put it through a strainer, heat up again, add pepper and salt, and serve hot.'

'That's fine,' said Coulibaly. 'But except for the salt and pepper, and the water too, there's none of those things back home. Perhaps that's the ideal. I must think about it seriously.'

'That's enough,' said the customs officer. 'We're friends.'

'Friends,' said Coulibaly.

They shook hands heartily, one smiling and the other puffing out his cheeks.

'You'll remember to send me a lion, won't you?'

'A lion?'

'Yes, a lion. Well, a lion's skin.'

'It's a promise,' said Coulibaly.

The captain was at his post too. Coulibaly went and greeted him. 'I put myself in your hands,' he began.

'All right,' the captain interrupted him. 'And how was your holiday?'

'It's over.'

'You went to Paris?'

'I went to Paris.'

'And did you go up the Eiffel Tower, did you visit the museums?'

The captain thought to himself: *Idiot! Why am I asking him that? A child like this doesn't need toys.*

Mockingly, he added: 'And the maritime museum, naturally?'

'And I didn't go up the Eiffel Tower,' Coulibaly replied. 'Nor did I visit the museums, not even the maritime one, naturally.'

Drop it! the captain told himself irately. *If I go on talking with this fellow, the ship will never sail.* Suddenly he remembered, and asked anxiously: 'And the trunks? Your precious trunks? You're not going to tell me . . .'

'The trunks?' said Coulibaly. 'Ah! the trunks . . . I left them in Paris, for my brother to have. He'll need them.'

DRISS CHRAIBI

The Remnants

The door opened and Haj Moussa came out with his human – late human – burden.

The people who saw him descend the seven steps from the front door, erect and dignified, not a quiver on his bony face, were passers-by and beggars, about a dozen all told. He reached the bottom step, and then they knew what he was carrying on his outstretched arms, which were as rigid and parallel as the arms of a stretcher. The people who were lying down rose to their feet as if startled by some catastrophe, those who were hurrying or strolling past suddenly stood still – and a moment later, arriving from nowhere, there was a dense and silent crowd; only the thousands of pairs of lips were moving, murmuring the Psalm for the Dead.

And so it happened: dressed all in white, his head covered and feet shod, carrying the body of his grandson (named Rachid for the registrar but whom he called 'the future generation') wrapped in a fine white shroud, he walked as stiffly as death and just as impervious to the full August sun that was making the shroud, the fronts of buildings and the pavements all gleam brightly; impervious to every human feeling, even suffering, and impelled only by the need to place one foot in front of the other, Haj Moussa passed through crowds that he did not even see, through streets that he had never set eyes on before and would never remember, walked straight ahead as though the whole town were empty and silent, as if walking through a fog which seemed to have the form and structure of a town but not the consistency; and everywhere he was seen the same sudden paralysis, the same abrupt heavy silence, came over people and things; and everywhere he passed (crossroads, streets and alleys) thousands of pairs of lips greeted him with the same faint whisperings, hurriedly mouthing the words and verses of the Psalm for the Dead.

When he entered the cemetery, practically the whole town was there behind him, a silent mass of women and children and old men, the hale and the infirm, people from all sides and of all ages, gathered there silent and grave as though at their own burial, so poignant is the death of a child, any child. But Haj Moussa did not look round. Even had he done so, he would have seen nothing, been unaware of their great presence, the soft breathing of thousands.

The gravedigger emerged from the hole he had hastily dug, cast aside his pick and spade and squatted down, the colour of dust up to his eyes. He had done his job well, like other men who make sandals or drive tractors.

'Wretched are we and turned to dust shall we be,' he said in a loud voice.

He saw, everybody saw, the old man in white step into the grave with the child's corpse and lay it down with the utmost gentleness, as though placing it in a cradle. As he stepped out again he was neither weeping nor even praying. He picked up the spade and began filling in the grave calmly and steadily. Then he squatted down and patted the mound of fresh earth, stroking and smoothing it as if tucking a sick child into bed. And he remained squatting with his armpits on his knees and with bowed head, but no longer smoothing and stroking a grave, a quite recent death, for his hands were wavering in front of his eyes – calming suffering, one would have said, all the sufferings of mankind, past, present, and future.

Much time passed before someone decided to hasten across, not to comfort him but to help him to his feet. A charitable soul left a group, crossed the ground with a measured step and held out a hand. Haj Moussa grasped it without thinking and started to rise. As he did so, his eyes encountered black leather boots, a dark uniform, and finally a black peaked cap. Standing against the

DRISS CHRAIBI The Remnants 63

setting sun, he saw the white armlet and the parcel wrapped in newspaper that the man was clasping under his arm. He met the eyes of this man standing stolidly in front of him – and, in a flash, his senses and memory returned, like the clashing of many cymbals.

'Here,' he said gently, pointing at the grave, 'here lies the future generation already. And the present generation doesn't even know it – he's in prison. And I, the past generation, I'm here to bear witness of our fate to everyone.'

'Just so,' said the policeman with some embarrassment, 'I was bringing you . . .'

'What?' cried the old man in a resounding voice. 'What have you brought me? Words? More words? More hopes? I'm telling you there are already three generations in this grave.'

He was still clutching the policeman's hand, and began pumping it up and down.

'I tell you that Rachid is dead, quite dead.' He punctuated his words with his action. 'I tell you that his father doesn't even know he's dead, doesn't even know he's been born. I don't know where his father is, you don't know where he is, and he doesn't know that he's had a son, that the son has had two years of earthly life and already has ten hours of *inexistence*. And now, what have you brought me? Official sympathy?'

'No,' said the policeman, more than ever embarrassed. 'Believe me, you have my sympathy in your great loss. Don't think that because I've a State uniform . . . Listen . . .'

But Moussa was no longer listening. He had turned away and was walking slowly towards the cemetery gate.

'Leave me alone,' he said, 'leave me in peace. I've been appealing to you for months, to try and find out where my son is. To discover which prison he is in. Why he was arrested. Who arrested him. If he really was arrested. To find out what breach of public order he was arrested for – and what is meant by a breach of public order. But you knew nothing about all that, policeman though you are, have been and always will be. So now leave me alone. You've brought me yet another hope? I don't know what that is. I shall know what hope means the day I understand the sense of a breach of public order in this society which is said to be humane, fraternal and free. Let me return in peace to my old house and wait for events to calm down of their own accord, like a thunderstorm or a flood. Let me return home and wait for my son to come back. For he'll come back one day, won't he? You see how patient I am. The last good turn of all that you can do me is to tell your superiors that I'm patience itself. Good day to you!'

He continued towards the gate. The other caught him up and made him take the parcel.

'The remnants,' he said hurriedly. 'I've been instructed to hand you what's left. Don't be angry with me, please. I'm only a man in uniform.'

Haj Moussa stood there stiffly, not understanding. Even when he had opened the parcel he still did not understand. The policeman had produced his notebook and was checking the contents of the parcel, avoiding the old man's eyes.

'One leather belt . . . one pair of tortoise-shell spectacles . . . one silk tie. Is that correct? Now, if you would just sign here, please . . .'

Moussa took the pen and signed. He had still not understood. It was only when everyone had left him, when the policeman had gone, the crowd had gone, when even the gravedigger had made off hurriedly, that Moussa *recognized* the tie, the spectacles and the belt – the remnants of his son.

The blood-red rays of the setting sun touched Haj Moussa as he toppled to the ground with the characteristic sound of a dead tree.

He used to say: 'In my age. In your age. The main thing, my son, is for your age to broaden out from mine.'

He used to say: 'Like a well-tried recipe that one improves on, like a patrimony that one transforms from a blazing torch into a glowing brazier, I shall not leave houses to you when I die – after all, they are nothing but old bricks – nor even banknotes, which are only pieces of paper, but something else. What you will inherit from me has a greater wealth, being of human quality; that is, an experience of life, a capacity to love and to have faith.'

He used to say: 'The age I lived in was a simple one, based on a society that has been agricultural and sedentary for centuries. The age you live in will be full of jiggery-pokery, struggles and courage. That's why I'm going to send you out into the new world, my son. I only hope you'll be happy, free and dignified, when you come back from this new world – as much as I've been, if not more so. That is what is called the evolution of people and races.'

So Haj Moussa sent his son out into the new world. When the holidays came round, he often noticed changes in his son, found him questioning certain tenets that had been the basis of his own world, and applying ideas and values that he himself had never heard of and could not even take in. However, he made no comment, even approved, for the changes he saw were in step with the new generation, with a whole mass of people.

Haj Moussa's son, fully qualified, close-shaven, active and keen, set himself up in a business quarter and from the very first was a pioneering spirit. He organized meetings, founded cultural clubs, undertook to educate those who had not had the opportunity to learn to read and write. Haj Moussa often went to see him in the evenings. He sat on the floor, on his prayer-mat, in keeping with ancient custom, and it gladdened his heart to look upon the four or five telephones all ringing at once, the typewriters clacking away, and, in the midst of this hive of industry, his son receiving callers, dictating and signing letters, giving orders. *I once had the opportunity of going over a factory*, Moussa was thinking. *I understood nothing about the working of it, and the noise almost made me deaf for good. But all that hurly-burly enabled dozens of people to earn a living, and outside I saw lorries being hastily loaded with manufactured goods which would help other people to live. That is all that matters.*

Then Haj Moussa rolled up his prayer-mat and went away rubbing his hands.

There came that morning, still so close yet so remote, like all grief and disaster. He had no foreboding. He pushed open the door and was met by silence, the silent typewriters and telephones, the silence of the whole building. With his prayer-mat under one arm, his hands shaking and eyes staring, he went round looking into all the rooms, even the cupboards, hoping every time he opened a door that by some miracle the sounds and activity of the hive would burst forth. But all he found was the silence, and in that silence he sat down, resigned in advance.

When night fell the caretaker came round to close the shutters, and knocked against him on opening a door. The caretaker stood there for a while, his hands clenched on the handle of the feather-duster in the pocket of his apron, looking down at the old man. A great feeling of pity ran through him like an electric shock; and so it happened that passers-by declared later that at seven o'clock that evening, just as the street lights came on, they had seen a man about six feet tall, with a feather-duster in his apron pocket, come out of the building carrying an old man in white whom he kept embracing and beseeching to forgive men's wickedness.

Dawn was breaking when the old man regained consciousness. He struggled to his feet, gathered up the remnants of his son and left the cemetery.

From that moment, everyone thought of him as a living corpse. He walked about like an automaton, with the jerky movements of a broken branch. He would seize people's hands and kiss them, bend down and kiss their knees, their bare feet or their sandals. But that was not why men and women fled from him. He sobbed like a lost child and talked to the empty air – but that was not why men and women fled. It was his eyes, huge, rolling eyes like those of a drug addict. Sometimes he spoke in a low moan and at other times he shouted, detaching each syllable.

'Old stones,' he would say, 'I'm going to leave old stones now, while I wanted so much to leave to future generations the achievements of my flesh, of my abilities to think and to love.'

DRISS CHRAIBI The Remnants

He would say — addressing anyone in the street, or even a
statue, a wall:

'Who wants a pair of spectacles? Or a silk tie? Who wants a
leather belt? Who wants me, all old skin and bone and with a
shrivelled heart?'

A workman in dungarees accepted the belt, another workman
dressed likewise in dungarees tried on the spectacles and took
them. Nobody wanted the tie. Haj Moussa attached it to an iron
ring on the wall at the corner of an alley, and put it round his
neck like a noose. Idle bystanders soon gathered round him; it
was only an old man dying, and they could do nothing, humanly
nothing, for this old fellow who had already died with his son —
whom he used to call the present generation and who had not
had the sense to run with the pack — and had died, too, with his
grandson whom he used to call the future generation and in
whom he had put so many hopes.

And so it came about — Haj Moussa was almost dead from
strangulation when a woman burst through the circle of on-
lookers, a dishevelled, screaming beggar-woman who cut the tie
with a penknife, helped up the old man and cleaved a way
through the crowd.

Nobody had the courage to follow those two. They were
already some way off, walking with measured tread, one supporting the other, cheering up the other with bursts of laughter that
were undoubtedly sobs. And they were quite sure that between
them, before long, they would present their fellow-men with
something other than banknotes or old stones — an achievement
of flesh and love, belief and hope.

They walked on with measured tread, laughing and sobbing
breathlessly. And, ahead of them, the sun suddenly shone from
the east.

HACÈNE FAROUK ZEHAR

Honour of a Drunkard[1]

It was the first time on a Sunday morning that I've woken up at seven o'clock and without any desire to shut my eyes again and stay in bed. As I always sleep until midday on Sundays, I felt rather at a loss. What should I do if I got up?

Last year, someone often asked me on a Saturday evening to go with him to the Flea Market the following day. I promised that I would, but when the alarm went off in the morning my enthusiasm stayed snug in the blankets.

But last year is over and done with; people now go chiefly to the market in human organs. I'd heard a lot about this place. For the past six months or so, the papers have been giving much space to these dealers in human spare parts. They are all eminent doctors, of course, but now that they make livers, hearts, and so on, they're all in competition with one another.

The first in the field soon made their fortunes. Just think – to begin with, every Head of State in the world had something in his organism that needed to be changed! Then came the big industrialists, and after them the film stars. They were followed by the wealthy middle-class, most of whom have stomachs of inordinate size. In the meantime, the expectation of life among the other classes of society had not changed. Before long, civil servants began using money put aside for the annual holiday on the purchase of a new eye or a nose, no matter what, especially as prices were falling all the time, though still remaining very high.

It sometimes happened that instead of, say, the gall-bladder it was the pancreas that should have been changed. This was a fatal error.

[1] The original title *Foi d'Ivrogne* contains a pun on the words *foi* (faith) and *foie* (liver) that is impossible to translate into English.

As I'm still young (according to the mirror, what people say, and my identity card), I've not deemed it necessary so far to change any of my innards. And it wasn't for lack of money. To be sure, I was neglecting to take into account the disorders of my liver. But I reasoned like this – in the event of a serious attack, I had only to take my car and drive speedily to the market. Unless it happened to be a Monday; then, like the butchers', the market is closed.

In these times, thank heaven, the possibility of engine trouble or even running out of petrol, can be excluded.

Well, as I happened to be wide-awake so early and had nothing to do, I thought I'd go and have a look round this market. If I set my heart on it, I could buy myself a new liver.

The idea appealed to me. I had a bath, washing myself all over, and with the water dripping from me on to the bathroom tiles I selected a clean towel, the colour of violets, to dry myself . . .

I went briskly down the stairs, got the car out of the garage and drove away without haste. It was half-past eight. I lowered the window, although the morning was still chilly. But there was a tang in the air, good to breathe as I glimpsed the trees slipping past.

The weather was neither fine nor bad. The pale yellow disc of the sun, however, was just beginning to show through the clouds.

All the parking spaces were taken; it was like arriving at a fair. I just left the car half on the pavement, and started to walk up the steep narrow street.

There were crowds about, but I was in no hurry. What should I do if I went back home straight away? Besides, in my haste to come away I had forgotten to have breakfast! So I went into the first café I came to and edged my way towards the counter, for the place was crammed. Each time I lifted my cup, I had to put it down again quickly for fear of spilling the coffee, so often did people bump into me. There were a lot of Americans, all bawling and drinking away. There must be some brawls here sometimes! And a few dead bodies, still warm, or who'd come to restore their youth.

They were trying to wear out their livers before casting them away.

Suppose I did the same? But I don't fancy drinking by myself, I need a companion or two.

In the midst of this, I felt as if I was at a market, but a weekly market as back home in my own country, where, at every town of any size, on Tuesdays, Wednesdays or Thursdays and from four or five in the morning onwards, you can see people coming in from different directions, riding donkeys or mules, or on foot, and herding along some cattle or goats or a flock of sheep. Other people arrive in lorries or vans that make you wonder by what miracle they had got to market, so old and battered is each one and so overloaded with horses, live chickens and dried skins, with sacks containing all kinds of country produce, with crates and baskets heaped together all anyhow, and I always wondered when the driver had managed to get a driving-licence and how the poultry could endure the journey and not die of suffocation or from being shaken about in the stifling atmosphere and among all the excrement.

Bah! Market or no market, I was going to do the same as these Americans.

'Whisky for me, please.'

The first mouthful went straight down to my stomach, arriving like a cool lump. The second met a warm gust that had just reached my throat. The third, the fourth and the rest got all mixed together; at the same time, a slight feeling of well-being came over me and I had a fit of the shivers.

I called for another glass, and went back to my weekly market. By five in the afternoon all that remains of the animation and the buying and selling of the morning are some flute-players in one corner, some storytellers in another, and, a little way off, snake-charmers and a few belated dealers trying to sell off large mounds of dates, dried figs or jujubes, tangerines, olives, measuring them out by the gallon more than anything, pouring them back and measuring out again, stroking one heap or another and patting it into a perfectly conical shape, while the sun goes down towards

America and the last of the loiterers shamble away, leaving some young scamps who pinch what they can and dart off, while the dealers hurl insults after them, some intended for their degenerate parents, and spit in disgust – tfou – near the heaps of fruit, on which the lazy, quick flies keep settling as fast as they are chased away.

I asked the brute who had just clapped me heavily on the left shoulder for a light. He picked up my drink and gulped it down, then turned to his pals and roared with laughter. I wasn't keen on having a fight. I called for another glass and drank it all, thereby showing that once was enough; but no one was taking notice of me any more, and so much the better.

I felt my liver, digging a finger under my right ribs as a doctor would have done. It hurt a little, and so much the better too; the more it hurt, the more I could congratulate myself on the step I was taking this morning.

I once went to be examined by a doctor. 'No cooked fats, no alcohol . . . cut out this, don't eat that . . .' and blah, blah, blah. As it happens, I like rich sauces, and when I visit my parents in future I'll be able to have a good tuck-in at home and also in the eating-houses of the town. For instance, get my teeth into one of those slices of bread spread with fried sardines done in garlic and red peppers, followed by a stew of beetroot and potatoes with large pieces of meat in it, of upland lamb; then, in another restaurant, order a huge dish of *kuskus*, and curds and whey and farm butter, and have some of those long green pimentoes in olive-oil served to me, hot to the taste and sharpening the appetite, and I'll eat them by the dozen . . .

In the late afternoon, having been for a swim, I'll have no qualms about going and propping up the bar-counter of one of those little café-restaurants along the sea-front which reek with the smell of chopped livers and hearts being broiled on small spits over a brazier, and I'll order dozens of them, or rather by the half-dozen so that they don't get cold. There'll be little dishes of shrimps, of boiled beans sprinkled with cumin, of split-peas and sliced sausage, placed around my glass of aniseed, and I'll nibble at these and then alternate between portions of kidney and of sheep's-head, *bouzellouf* as they're called. When my broiled livers and hearts are ready, I'll decide on a bottle of *rosé*, nicely chilled. Then I'll go and sit down to have shoulder of mutton *à la mechoui*, with a big raw onion to bite at now and again; that helps the digestion.

However, as I wasn't over there in the sunshine, I had another whisky, a double this time, so that I should have a hazier view of the people around me. Ever since I'd stepped inside this café, they had not stopped laughing, shouting, and swiping at one another.

In here you could have, if you liked, if you liked to pay for them, peanuts and salted almonds and packets of potato-crisps.

The ideal place to be at, actually, would be a country inn I know in Provence. Madame Corvelle, the plump little woman of fifty who keeps it, serves lunch and dinner to about forty people, always the same ones. She provides, in addition to her motherly charms, the best and cheapest meals in the region . . .

I was game! I was all for it – that was what I was trying to make the blockhead who had gulped down one of my drinks understand, but he wouldn't listen. He was trying to remember the address of a restaurant he had been told about, where – so he said – the food was served by naked women who, if you wished, would take you to their room, even between two courses.

It would be wrong of me to pretend that I knew the place; but I've been in so many others of the kind, especially back home. The peasants who go to the weekly market make for the 'red-light district' in the evening, each wrapped in his *burnous*, a *chechia* on his head, a piece of leather tied with string for footwear, unshaven, eyes shining, yearning for the pleasures of the town, craving for drink and women, all women, the wives of the shoemakers, the greengrocers, and the officials, and for the officials' daughters, indecent European girls in tight skirts that show the hem of their knickers; and these peasants, it is said, or was said, even cast sidelong glances at young boys, whom they describe between themselves as dainty, a bad lot and ill-mannered, comparing them with their own children who get up early to go and work in the fields, but who, as is well known, are not necessarily little saints.

These rustics arrive timidly at their destination, give a generous tip to the brothel-house keeper and step inside a place well-known to them through having visited it every week for years past, sneak in rather, hoping not to be seen by some relative or some magistrate before whom they might be called one day, or by some tax official who could hold it against them that they had been in places where men spent money, whereas in matters of taxation they were always pleading poverty.

Behind me, one of the Americans seemed to be snorting like a horse; I turned round and saw him with his legs firmly apart and body swaying, holding out a half-full bottle of whisky in his right hand; he knocked the top off with a sweeping blow of his left hand, and faced up to a couple of toughs wearing leather jackets over their rollneck sweaters. I turned away . . . there came to mind a somewhat similar scene in one of those brothels I had been thinking about . . . It was the first time I had tasted beer! That day, I had looked on with eager eyes as two *burnous*-clad peasants confronted one another with their sticks (of olive-wood, slender and gnarled); their *chechias* had fallen off, and their shaved heads presented targets for the violent blows they aimed at each other, parrying, thrusting, hitting out and missing, while around them was a confusion of chairs and tables, bottles and glasses, all strewn across the tiled floor. The men and women had drawn back against the walls or retreated into corners; one of the duellists suddenly put a hand to his ear, which was streaming with blood, soaking into his white *gandoura*, and his lips drew right back to reveal shiny white teeth as he sank to the floor.

And behind me they were knocking each other about and making empty threats, not having the guts to call it off, reeking of false courage and whisky. Braggarts . . .

I had another drink. I'd have willingly left, if only they'd finish tearing each other to pieces, and if I hadn't been reminded of certain mishaps in the life of my grandfather, whom I never knew, as told by his son, thanks to whom or through whose fault

F

I had seen the light of day; and the thought of one unforgettable incident kept me standing at the bar, while around me it looked like ending with the death of someone, over whom would be shed one, two or a thousand tears – of whisky, obviously – in order to forget and also to become belligerent again.

One night, my grandfather surprised some cattle-thieves in his farmyard; they were whacking at the cattle and had already driven about a hundred out of the corral. My grandfather, though conciliatory and peace-loving by nature, whirled his staff and brought it down on the nearest available head. He was at once surrounded by a score of threatening figures all wielding a stick of some kind.

Grandfather would probably have preferred to talk the matter over. But a blow on his left shoulder promptly caused him to amend his usual manner of reacting. Lashing out with his stick, he retreated backwards into the night. And the story goes – it was this point especially which had come to my mind – that he covered fifteen miles in this fashion, until the sun rose, beaten back by the thieves who only gave up at the gates of the nearest town. Retreating backwards for fifteen miles!

Well, there I still was, leaning against the bar-counter; one of the Americans was stretched out on the seat along the wall, another was sprawled over the counter with his bloody head resting on it, rolling the whites of his eyes as he kept trying to jerk his head up, then letting it fall again like a stone, which gave me a start each time and made me pull my own head up, for – as I became aware – my chin was touching my chest.

I could barely make out people's forms, they were all quivering and swaying and merging one into another at ever-varying speeds.

The time had come, it seemed, to put my intention into effect. I tottered out, shouldering my way through the throng without troubling to look back; I was in a hurry. Just one more effort, a new liver, and a new life would open before me!

I thought it would be an open market, freely accessible. I'd no idea there would be this old lady sitting in a sort of ticket-office, as at a cinema or a football-ground, or like a seller of lottery tickets in her little kiosk.

Just inside the entrance were two girls in uniform, chattering away. I was about to protest at having to pay before being served, but the woman at the cash-desk looked up and at once asked me: 'What number is your ticket?'

'Number? Ticket?'

'Ah, so you haven't registered?'

There's a disappointment for you! In order to have my liver changed, cash down, I first had to go and register at the town hall of my borough. And, of course, pay taxes and stamp-duty, queue for official papers of all kinds – and wait for at least six months to be told to go along with my card and numbered ticket.

I didn't wait to hear any more.

I retraced my steps, feeling bitter. People bumped into me, but I took no notice; my walk was heavy and so was my heart. Of course, I could pull a few strings to hasten the procedure, now that I was set on the idea. Still, a market ought to be open to all. But this one wasn't!

I supposed that there must be a section reserved for urgent cases in this dispensary of happiness, that the need of a numbered ticket would be waived in the event of an accident. And how about payment? The old lady had told me that you paid in advance at the town hall and at the same time you took out a sort of insurance-policy enabling you to obtain a refund and to apply again if, for one reason or another, you were unable to attend the market when summoned. Yes, that was what the old lady had said.

So there I was, up against a system again, drunk and pessimistic. I came to the café I had left a short time before; the Americans were still yelling away and roaring with laughter, hitting out with fists and feet as and when they could, and missing more often than not. No, I thought, not there; I'll have a drink farther down.

I noticed a coal-merchant's, one of those old-fashioned little shops that sell coal in small quantities and wine and spirits too.

I had a whole string of reasons for not going in, but I stopped in front of the glass-panelled door and looked inside (probably with a glassy stare). It was the genuine thing, a good old *bougnat*'s, and I pushed the door open with my foot and at the same time tried to hold it from swinging back. I missed, and almost fell against the counter. The scruffy fellow on the other side, a villainous-looking man with bristling whiskers, held out a hand as big as a spade; I put mine in it, and it gripped and shook me vigorously several times until I began to feel annoyed and raised my head to get a proper look at this enthusiast who was treating me in such a manner, and I stammered, though badly wanting to blow my nose, to sneeze, and I growled on catching sight of my mug in the mirror – for I'd taken three steps to the left and the fellow with the whiskers had shifted sideways for a moment – and then I neither stammered nor growled but, propping my right elbow on the counter and holding my head high, I mumbled something once or twice, paused to laugh up my sleeve, then bellowed, 'The same again!'

The proprietor burst out laughing, slapped his thigh and looked across at – there were a good dozen of them, twenty or thirty even – the hairy, scruffy lot wearing caps or berets, sitting there playing cards, which they all dropped on the table, stopped sipping their thimblefuls of calvados, and began digging one another in the ribs and slapping one another on the back, looking at me, looking at each other and winking, so much so that I got annoyed for the second time; I banged my glass down on the first table I reached (what had he given me to drink?), leaned forward – to tell the truth, I couldn't do much, I was feeling sick – raised my glass and shouted several times, 'Your very good health!' A little surprised, not to say impressed, each of them raised his glass; and as they tilted their heads back, I emptied my glass on to the most convenient shock of hair and scurried back to the counter, wanting to vomit but swallowing the stuff again, sending it back to where it came from – there is a place for everything, a time for everything, and I had all of life in which to be sick. . . . But as soon as I was alone . . .

Another peal of laughter from the proprietor rose above the customers' ejaculations, and my uneasy conscience stilled as I heard someone say, 'Don't you know your friends now?' I turned quickly towards the door, but no one was there. 'The gentleman thinks he's somebody!' came a voice. Then I swung round to the counter again, knocking over my glass, as I realized it was Guillaume who was standing there looking at me with a jaunty air – Guillaume, whom I hadn't seen for years. He drew my head forward and embraced me, his moustache prickling my right cheek, and he exclaimed joyfully, 'He hasn't changed, it's just as I told you, he's still a good old sport, is my pal!'

His pal!

Beaming and talking away, he took me over to one of the tables. I was getting glum and weary again, and wanted to tell him about . . . But he gave me no chance. 'What would you like?' he said.

Slumped on my seat, I kept pulling the table towards me and pushing it back with my foot, without meaning to, and I couldn't help speaking of my anxiety, telling him of my fears and little troubles that morning.

'What, you?' he cried, shaking with laughter again, his saliva dribbling on to the cleaned table, just wiped down by I couldn't say whom. 'You?' he exclaimed again. 'They want you to go to the town hall? Not while I'm around!'

I couldn't help smiling. His dark eyes were fixed on me with an intentness that I knew of old, and he had suddenly become serious. 'You've lost confidence in your lucky star, you can't speak up for yourself, is that it?' he said. 'You've got married, maybe? What's happened to you?' he roared, giving my flabby shoulder a hard blow with his fist. 'What's got into you? How is it you've lost confidence, come on, explain . . .'

I tried, perforce, to explain. I talked of anything that came into my head. He, for his part, described the system governing the market – it was a racket, a mafia; friends in high places were of no help, you had to be a member! Listening to him, I knew he would fix things for me. Meeting him again was a real pleasure.

No problem ever got the better of him, not even for a moment. He knew how to take life, and his conscience was pure, more so than mine, which is a patchwork of embarrassment and reluctance. He meets difficulties half-way, while I always edge away from any hint of them. I am exactly what he is not; he is what I could never be.

Guillaume was already at the telephone, one hand holding the receiver and the other thrust into the top of his trousers, settling my problem for me without any anxiety or mistake. Yet there is nothing of the man of business about him. At ease in his little nook, the turmoil of everyday life passes him by.

He likes to hear me talk about duels with sticks in a brothel. Whenever I recall the experiences of my father or my grandfather, he listens intently, feeling each blow and lashing out in return, getting all agitated and letting fall exclamations like 'Ah, the dirty dog!' Drinks arrive on our table, and he shouts as if having a fight himself, 'I'll do you in, I'll lap up your blood!' Yet God knows he's a good chap.

However, we eventually set off, he supporting me but sometimes hanging on to my arm too. As we went along, Guillaume told me about the market. Once inside, you apparently followed a maze of corridors to reach the hall where people sat bearing their sufferings patiently for the last time. Among them were many women who had nothing wrong with their organism, but were there either from snobbery or to pick up someone. This reminded me, for some unknown reason, of my mother. When I was sixteen, she had said to me: 'I've always been virtuous, my son, and never have I been unfaithful to your father, neither in thought or deed. But I'll tell you one thing, my son – all women are whores!' I had said to myself that the exception proved the rule.

Guillaume had a steady hand and a step that, although hesitant, could not have been better for conducting someone like me, drunk and having little interest in anything other than my liver.

At the entrance to the market he said to me: 'I'm going to walk round to the other side; you know what to do, and I'll meet you there, when you come out you'll be as good as new. I've got another café round there, a real one. You'll like it, I know. You'll look upon it with your new liver and you'll find life good, I promise you!'

The old lady in her ticket-office did not look up as I passed, she just held out her hand; I shook it and passed on. One of the girls in uniform came over to me. 'You have number fourteen thousand two hundred and forty-eight, serial fifteen. Follow me, please.'

I staggered drunkenly after her. She walked quickly, and I managed to keep up solely, so it seemed, because of her behind, the effect of which was apparently studied for the benefit of people with liver complaints; it swayed so much this way and that, I never lost courage. The concrete floor was seesawing under my feet and I went up and down, more down than up as the uniformed behind gradually drew away from me, but I meant to get there even if it were on all fours.

I sprawled forward on the floor. It was so silly and shameful. When her ankles were a yard from me, I got up and heard myself say, 'At this rate, we'd better get a move on!'

Again there was the behind in front of me, but having no effect now; I had to keep after it, however, for it was my only guide. I saw her stop and press a button to call the lift. The door slid open just as I reached it, so I surged into the lift without slowing my pace. And up we went.

I was tempted to . . . Idiot! As if I couldn't have patience a little longer. Guillaume was waiting for me at the other end, and many joys and pleasures with him.

More corridors, more stairs, numbered doors, directional signs, intersections and turnings, deadly silence, tapping heels, the girl's heels going one-two, one-two. I was fed up.

I had a great desire to turn back, to run and get out of the place! But I couldn't have run if I'd tried, and in any case I should never have found the way out, especially as – I'd almost forgotten – you didn't go out the way you'd come in. So be it. As that was the way of things, it was no good pretending they were otherwise.

I had noticed a similar kind of thing when on a visit to London.

One evening, having lingered, shall we say, in a pub, at eleven
o'clock I was given to understand that I must finish my drink
and leave the premises. This had riled me. 'There's a new law in
your country,' I cried, 'that Her Majesty the Queen has approved,
and you know nothing about it! It's a law that applies only to
foreigners – they can't be turned out like this, and quite right too!
They weren't consulted when you made the law that pubs have
to close at eleven.' At that, a huge fellow had planted himself in
front of me and, as I was unable to raise my head, I just saw his
hands come to rest on his hips. 'I don't want to be a nuisance,' I
said, my chin still on my chest. 'Let me have just one more bottle
of beer, and I'll drink it outside.'

'Honest?'

'Honest. Take the top off for me, though. I've nothing to do
that with.'

When I'd been given the bottle of beer and had paid for it, I
put it to my lips and drank the lot there and then. Insults were
hurled at me from all sides, and the women who were there urged
the chucker-out to give me what I deserved. But he held back,
not being too sure about me. And I had gone off chanting, in
English naturally, 'The law is the law.'

However, there was now no question of turning back. I was in
the huge waiting-room that Guillaume had told me about, and I
almost sobered up at the sight – all those people, there to avoid
dying! They all had anxious expressions that seemed to be
hanging on the kind of clocks high along the far wall, one for
each lot of serial numbers probably; every now and again a red
light flashed on, then a number showed, and one of the waiting
people hurried towards a door numbered six or five, fourteen or
two, and disappeared.

I realized that all I had to do now was to await my turn.

I happened to overhear a little old white-haired man, all
bowed and wizened, having a sharp argument with a young man
in his early twenties.

'You're not at my stage yet, you've got plenty of time!' the
old man was saying. 'I know there's no risk for you, otherwise I

shouldn't be asking you to do this for me. I'd ask the same thing of my son, if he were still alive! Come now, it's not a serious matter for you, but it's very important to me! Look, if you're so heartless, I'll tell you what I'll do . . .'

'I'm not to be bought, monsieur,' the young man cut in. 'As I've already told you, I'd normally do it with pleasure. Today I can't, I must go through as soon as possible, it's of fundamental importance. My reasons are not so good as yours, you say; very well then, find someone else, and don't waste time. I can't afford to miss my appointment. I appreciate your difficulty, but I can't do anything about it!'

The old man seemed to shrivel up a little more, his face quivered, and he looked altogether pitiful, staring at the clocks as though the numbers were not appearing quickly enough for him. He took off his hat and ran his fingers through his white hair; then, with shaking hands and a sob in his voice, he began pleading again.

I had realized by then that he was asking the young man to part with his number, fearing that his own would be called too late. But the young man still refused, repeating that his life and his love were likely to be ruined if he were late for his appointment! The old man might collapse at any moment, but the other, through being after a new penis or something of the kind, wanted nothing to do with him.

Behind me, two women were confiding in one another, and I gathered that one was going to replace her left breast, which drooped more than its neighbour.

I ought to have taken some sandwiches with me! There were all those corridors, the tickets and registrations, but no one had been smart enough to think of opening a snack-bar. Now if I were in business . . . !

A red light had been on for a good two minutes. The number was 14,248, serial fifteen! Old Guillaume was a wonder, no doubt about it. I practically ran. . . .

In the first room, I was placed on a wheeled stretcher, but not strapped down.

In the second room, I was given a pill.

Third room – I remember nothing about that.

In the last room but one I was stood on my feet, and when I reached the last room of all I was told not to worry, everything was paid for. That was fine.

I found Guillaume looking very downcast. While I had been rejuvenating myself, he had tried to lure two women into his place, two women who had left the market a quarter of an hour before me. I tried to joke about it, but he kept saying, 'If you'd seen her bosom! And not wearing a bra, I could tell that all right!'

'You'll come across others . . .'

'Oh no, not like that. While I was waiting for you, I'd have liked to . . . And afterwards . . .'

'Afterwards, what?'

'Why, have the other one, of course, if you'd been a little longer!'

He seemed to have recovered his jovial spirits, and at the door of his 'real' café he leaned towards me to confide in a pathetic tone: 'You know, there's one thing I'll never have changed.'

'What's that?'

'Well, the . . . you know, my . . .'

'Your tool?'

'Yes, that's it, my tool. I'll never change that.'

'But a time's bound to come when . . .'

'No, I mean it. Never that.'

'Well then, how . . . ?'

'I'll retire, old chap, I'll go into retirement.'

Then he told me that he was giving a party to celebrate our meeting again, and ushered me towards the bar.

AHMED SEFRIOUI

The Earthenware Jar

In which the white page becomes covered with black characters.

Abdallah lives in order to build. He is a mason by trade and a poet from birth. The people of the town know this, and never give him any work to do. Can one let a poet build one's house?

I share a small room with Abdallah, and we get on well together. It is possible for a carpet-maker-theologian and a poet to live under the same roof, eat from the same bowl and pray five times a day to the same God without harming each other unduly. We have no luxurious tastes and we wear shabby clothes. We eat, sleep, and give praise to our Creator on the same mat. During my idle hours I turn the pages of a thick *Ghazali* which has comments, notes and references. This massive volume of poems constitutes my sole wealth and contains enough nourishment for my mind to last me until the grave.

Abdallah never reads, but he fills whole pages with black, well-spaced characters. These pages lie dormant between two sheets of grey cardboard. They result from hours of inertia during which Abdallah seems dead to his surroundings. However, of all this mass of writing, I know only the following story. I am hesitant about telling it, for it may be thought quite ordinary and my trouble quite unnecessary. Never mind. I shall tell it just as my companion put it down, after long meditation, in black characters on his white page.

For two days Abdallah had reclined on his palm matting, staring into space with moonstruck eyes. He ate very little, spoke even less, and never once quitted his dim corner of the room. On

the morning of the third day he sat up, put a board across his
knees and spread a fine white sheet of paper in front of him, a
sheet so white that it shed a gentle light about the dusky room,
like that on a starlit night. Dipping a reed-pen in black ink, he
began to cover the sheet feverishly with letters. They flowed
erratically, running into one another, separated and then re-
joined, formed into pyramids and then spread out again. The
lines piled up, the blank space grew smaller. Late at night
Abdallah was still writing by the light of an oil-lamp. The sheet
was filled with characters. Abdallah stretched out on his bedding,
then gave me the sheet of paper to read. I took some time to make
out what he had written, and when that task was done I looked
up and said to him:

'This is a lovely story, about the potter.'

'There's no question of a potter in that story.'

I read it again, then declared with a triumphant air: 'I quite
understand your story about a florist.'

'There's no question of a florist in that story.'

I copied it all out, and now and again I show it to my friends.
But none has ever yet told me what it all means.

The story goes like this:

A potter who loved his jars.

With what care did he choose his clay, with what love did he
sprinkle pure water on it, and with what respect did he knead
this basic mud! One can create only in joy. This joy mingled with
pain, from which life issues, caused the potter's fingers to
tremble with almost sacred delight. Jars are living things,
similar yet varied at the same time, images of one of the numerous
possibilities of the Manifestation; they are born of earth, water,
air and fire. Whoever knows the secret of the principle of gyra-
tion becomes as God! Potter, is it really your own will bringing into being that earthy flower which is taking shape under
your hand? Then you have ceased to be the man doomed
to eat his bread by the sweat of his brow. No, no vain pride,
you little worm! Your will is but the pale reflection of

His will. And the man who is aware of that, has a labour of love.

However, Ba Driss knew all the secrets and had great ardour. But the Evil One sets cleverly disguised traps.

Ba Driss had got up late that morning. In the cool shade of his workroom the well-prepared heaps of clay, all impurities removed, were awaiting him in orderly array. He took off his *djellaba,* jumped into the ditch and set the wheel humming. A bluish gleam brightened up the humid temple. And until evening Ba Driss modelled his big-bellied jars, pressing with the thumbs of an impassive god and watching them take shape. There were rows and rows of them, dozens and still more dozens. His day's work finished, he prepared to leave. The silhouette of a beggar loomed in the doorway. The setting sun was framing his shoulders in copper and strewing precious powder over his patched hood.

He held out his hand to the potter and said:

'I appeal to your good heart, feed the beggar.'

He spoke in a flat, impersonal voice, rather like that of a ventriloquist.

The potter fumbled in his *chekkara* and found a coin that he gave to the beggar without a word. The latter stayed there, tucked the coin away in the folds of his rags and said again:

'I appeal to your good heart, feed the beggar.'

The ritual phrase echoed back: 'May God make it possible.'

For a third time, like a worn-out mechanism, the disquieting voice uttered the phrase: 'I appeal to your good heart, feed the beggar.'

Ba Driss, his throat gone dry and a cold sweat on his brow, had just the strength to raise his eyes to the ceiling and cry:

'O Lord God! I seek refuge in Thee against Satan, the wiles of sorcerers and the attacks of the envious!'

The dark figure bent forward and sent a stream of spittle over the jars, then melted away in the last rays of an apocalyptic sun.

.   .   .   .   .

The jars dried in the shade. They were carefully placed in the kiln and subjected to a fierce heat. The flames cleansed them of their taint and, like the hand of Moses, when drawn forth they were free of all defilement.

Ba Driss began to sort them. The first jar he examined had a wide crack in it from top to bottom. With a sigh, he put it to one side. But the second was the same, and the third too, and all the others. Yes, all without exception had the awful defect which made them unusable.

Slumped among the ruins of so much effort and tender care, the potter bowed his head in silence. He stroked the rounded form of one of these earthenware carcasses. Deep in his dismal thoughts, he stared unseeingly at the perfect curve of one he had just touched. Suddenly, his eyes cleared and he saw that it was quite intact. With a cry of joy he started to check all the jars, but alas! only that one had escaped the spell. He clutched it reverently to his chest plastered with dried mud, raised his eyes in supreme adoration and murmured:

'O Lord God! I seek refuge in Thee against Satan, the wiles of sorcerers and the attacks of the envious!'

A florist who loved his flowers.

The potter had a friend. He sold flowers in a tiny booth at 'Ras Cherratine'. It was an ideal spot for a florist. There was a fountain murmuring away close by. Students from the near-by *medersa* treated themselves to a bouquet when roses were in bloom, and the barber opposite used large amounts of medicinal plants. People came from the farthest parts of the town to buy palms to put on graves and cuttings for their gardens. Passers-by admired the booth's fine show, which gave a splash of colour to the street.

In spring and summer, autumn and winter alike, a neatly dressed, wizened old man could be seen rummaging in this verdant setting, among the gleam and sparkle of freshly-watered petals.

The whole town knew Ba Sidi. An unknown poet had written a song about him and the refrain was on everyone's lips:

'Ba Sidi! Ba Sidi!
Your beard is a broom of silk.
Ba Sidi! Ba Sidi!
Your turban is fit for a king.'

It was a Tuesday when the potter went to see Ba Sidi in his garden, as he insisted on calling what was actually an abandoned cemetery, one of the many to be found at the end of a blind alley. There he had gathered jars of all shapes and sizes, enamel bowls of every colour, cracked vases, worn-out cooking-pots and rusty old cans. From each of these discards there sprang the blaze of a rose, the delightful pattern of a double carnation or the brilliance of a buttercup. Ba Sidi kept careful watch over this paradise haunted by goldsmith-beetles and sun-drenched butterflies. He remained contemplating his little world for hours on end, his deep-set eyes smiling happily from under their woollen tufts; and now and again he gently stroked his beard with a hand whose back was covered with veins and white hairs. He was engaged in this innocent pastime when the potter arrived and roused him from his blissful state. They had known each other a long time, and the potter received a warm welcome.

'I've brought you a new jar,' he said. 'If God so wills, it shall hold a wonderful flower.'

'All flowers are wonderful things,' the old man replied. 'They are pleasing and make good company. For many long years now, I have seen them blossom, live, and die. I've scarcely begun to understand them. Life is short, alas, and I shall pass away long before fathoming their secret. They seem to me to hold the secret of Creation even. But don't tell anyone of my heretical remarks. Show me this jar.'

Ba Driss stood a jar with shapely curves on the ground, and the two looked at it in silence.

The potter was the first to speak. 'I can see an emerald branch sprouting from this vase, crowned with a cluster of rubies. Or would you prefer a corona of dazzling sunlight?'

'Perhaps, perhaps,' the old man gravely replied.

He remained wrapped in thought for a few moments, then leaned towards the potter with a mysterious air and whispered in his ear:

'I'd use it to grow the flower with a thousand petals, but for that it has to be pure.'

He nodded to himself and said again, 'It has to be pure.'

The holy man.

On the Friday, as the faithful were coming out of the mosque and being assailed by beggars, a voice was heard singing:

> 'Free God of the shades of darkness
> That are stifling Him,
> The image of thy love
> Will flower there.'

It was the old florist who was intoning the words of this strange incantation, his eyes fixed on an earthenware jar. The news spread through the town – Ba Sidi was 'touched by God'. His booth became covered with votive offerings.

He went on untiringly repeating the same refrain, head bent and eyes lowered.

When the flow of believers had dwindled, someone approached the old man. No one had seen this person before; he was wearing white clothes that smelt of Paradise. He walked with measured tread, looking neither to right nor to left. He said not a word to anyone. Ba Sidi, still with lowered head, stopped his slow chanting. The stranger stood over him, tall and upright. Ba Sidi made no movement. Then the other slowly bent down, took a pinch of dust, a little of the dust trodden by the faithful as they came out of the mosque, and let it fall from his fingers into the earthenware jar. Ba Sidi staggered like a drunken man, seized his jar and tottered off with it.

Two days later, his friend the potter found him lying dead in his garden among the roses and narcissi. He was holding his earthenware jar in his arms. Light was flooding from it, and at the bottom the incandescent rays of a strange flower dazzled the sight. Everyone was able to admire this wonder.

Ba Sidi was buried with his jar. And two doves came and wept on the grave.

MOULOUD MAMMERI

An Episode from
Le Sommeil du Juste

[*The time is 1940, in a mountain village of Kabylia. The two main characters, Arezki and Sliman, are the sons of a poor villager who believes himself cursed because an ancestor committed murder three centuries ago. Arezki has been educated at French schools and has just passed the entrance examination to a Teachers' Training College. Between him and his father there is utter incomprehension.*

Arezki has blasphemed in front of the village elders, saying that God does not exist. His father goes to get his gun, and Arezki runs away.]

When the father returned home late that night, so that no one should see him, he was quite glad to have missed hitting Arezki; glad, too, at having turned him out.

He realized however that the departure of Arezki solved nothing. It was that school-teacher at Tasga who was putting ideas into his son's head; but how could he discuss the matter with the teacher? He knew no French and the teacher knew no Berber. He thought of the commissar.

The commissar was the administrator, in other words the head of the district. These infidels all speak the same language and think in the same manner; the wrong way, maybe, but in the same manner.

The father, as it so happened, had been wanting to see the commissar for some time. His eldest son, Mohand, had tuberculosis and three children. It was while working at the Renault factory in Paris that Mohand had contracted tuberculosis, and Paris is in France and the commissar French so it was only right that he should give Mohand a pension; just a small pension, say two or three thousand francs, but two or three thousand francs is better than nothing.

Then there was Sliman, the youngest, who of course had never been to school but whom his father would dearly like to send 'over to Renault's', as he had Mohand; but Mohand always said he would kill his kid brother first, and with that disease which was eating away his chest you could never tell. 'You know, young 'un, it'd be better to die by my hand than to be eaten away by tuberculosis, for at least you wouldn't suffer.' Mohand never laughed when he said that, not even his deep and bitter laugh. So then his father wondered if the commissar could get his youngest son into an apprentice school for masons.

'Why a school for masons?' asked Mohand.

His father could only say, with a shrug, 'Because it's a fine thing to build houses.'

Mohand's sarcastic laugh ended in a bout of coughing which made his face go purple as if the blood were about to spurt through his cheeks. 'So you believe we choose a trade because it's a worthy one; we go out to work because we're starving. You think the commissar is a labour exchange – that he's been sent here to teach a trade to sons of the poor. He's in charge of the whole district, the commissar is – and do you know how many Slimans, how many sons of poor people there are in the commissar's district? Is the commissar going to make thousands of masons of them?'

'Someone has to think about the sons of poor people.'

'God! They have God, the sons of the poor.'

He laughed. His father sensed that Mohand was on the point of blasphemy – like the other son. He couldn't go and kill all of them! Besides, this one was ill.

Yet the father remained obstinately hopeful; men whom God has set in charge over others are meant to work for the happiness of the children of the poor. They are destined for that good fortune. How wonderful it is, how good to work for the happiness of men, of all men! It is so much more wonderful than ploughing the fields or working in a factory. What finer destiny is there than to be set in charge of the happiness of men ? Mohand stifled his laugh for fear of coughing.

His father's plan was a simple one. When Mohand's time came to die (only God is eternal), leaving behind his wife and his three young children, two boys and a girl, Arezki would marry Mekioussa, the widow of his elder brother, according to custom. Arezki would become a school-teacher; he would therefore earn good money. Sliman would become a mason, which is a fine trade. He would get married too. And that would bring an end to the poverty which had faithfully kept step with the head of the family for the whole of his sixty years.

Chance helped his plans, for the following Friday he went to market and while there a trooper came to tell him that the administrator wished to see him.

He followed the man. The administrator was certainly going to talk to him first of all about the rifle shot; but when he had finished explaining the administrator would understand, and then he could take the opportunity to speak to him first about the school-teacher at Tasga, who was diverting Arezki from the straight path; and then, above all, about the other two, Mohand and Sliman.

The commissar was seated behind a table which seemed to the father immoderately long. He had naturally heard about administrators but had never seen one before. This one appeared to him to be dressed rather like a gendarme.

The father went in without saying a word and remained standing in front of the desk, not knowing what to do with his hands. The administrator slowly raised his eyes, looked at him and, as though he had suddenly lost his wits, said something to him in Arabic. The father made no reply, and the administrator rose from his chair, again in a rage, and jabbered something or other.

A trooper entered, and in a rather arrogant manner asked him why he did not answer. 'Has everyone gone mad here?' thought the father. He replied: 'Tell him that I don't understand Arabic.'

The trooper translated.

'The administrator asks you if you can speak French?'

'No, I can't,' said the father. 'I come from Ighzer. There isn't a school in our village.'

The trooper translated back. The same frenzy overcame the administrator, shaking his legs, arms and hands, and making all his features twitch.

'The administrator says that he hasn't summoned you here for you to give your opinion on what goes on in the district.'

'I was only answering a question he put to me. But if I said anything that offended him, I ask his pardon.'

The administrator said something that the interpreter thought it better not to translate.

Then: 'The chief asks what language you do speak.'

'Berber.'

'The administrator wants to know why you can't speak French like everyone else.'

'Tell him, if it won't offend him, that Berber is the tongue of my forefathers.'

The interpreter did not translate; no doubt that too would be taken as an affront. The commissar's mind seemed to work in such a very queer way.

The interview continued, slowly and with difficulty, because each time it was necessary to go through the interpreter and you couldn't be very sure what that fellow, with his curled moustache and arrogant yet listless eyes, was making of your words.

It seemed to the father that the commissar and he were on sticky ground and making enormous but vain efforts to get near each other. He tried to be meek and conciliating, stretching out a hand as far as he could to reach the other; but, O God, how far away the other was, how very far away!

Nevertheless, he did eventually understand what it was all about; the commissar had learnt that his entire family was harbouring evil intentions against the administration. Sliman, especially, had joined a so-called People's Party (scum, the whole lot of them) and was helping the terrorists, who pretended to be

patriots but were really highway robbers. The commissar could
easily chuck Sliman into prison for the rest of his days, but he
took his youth into account, and before taking such a step
preferred to talk to the father. He was the head of the family, was
he not? Then it was up to him to lead his son back to the right
path. In the meantime, just to make them realize (and the son
especially) to what extent the administration was necessary to
them, the commissar was withdrawing all the family's ration-
cards. 'And he can go and complain to the Pope, if he likes.'

The father tried to make the commissar see reason. It seemed
to him most unlikely that his son had joined a *sof*, without at least
letting him know or talking it over with him; in any case, he was
going to find out about it and, if it were true, would cure Sliman
of any desire ever to do the same thing again. However, said the
father, he could not manage without ration-cards.

'The admistrator asks whether you want to go to prison straight
away?'

The father could hardly get over the fact that one man could
speak to another in such a way, and say such heedless things; but
does not the proverb say that if you imitate the madman you are
as mad as he? He forced himself to keep calm.

'How are we going to eat?' he said.

He saw the commissar laugh, then the other translated. 'The
administrator tells you to go and ask the party leader for bread.'

The father did not understand what was meant by these words.

'I am poor,' he said, 'and I have a large family.'

'Eat less or breed fewer.'

The father made no reply. He recalled his conversation with
Mohand: those whom God has set in charge over other men . . .
what finer destiny than to work for men's happiness? Was that
what he had said? Was it he? He heard the sarcastic, blasphemous
voice of Mohand: the sons of the poor have God, the rich have
the administrators.

'Dreaming, old 'un?' said the interpreter in Berber. 'You're
lucky to be able to dream, you are. I haven't time to. Come on,
hand them over.'

One by one the father brought out the ration-cards and counted them into the other's hand. 'That's mine, that's the card of my children's mother. My son's, and my daughter-in-law's. This one is his.'

'What d'you mean – his?'

'Sliman's.'

He handed them all over.

'Tell him that he'll have them back when we get definite proof that his son is no longer acting the fool.'

The father remained standing there, his arms dangling, shaking his head now and then; as the commissar seemed to have nothing more to add, he said at last: 'May I go?'

He no longer had any desire to speak about the schoolmaster at Tasga, nor Mohand, and certainly not about Sliman.

'Clear off,' said the trooper.

The father looked for the door.

'No, wait,' called the commissar. 'Ask him if he has a clear conscience.'

The father was dumbfounded. Was it possible that he whom God had called to govern men could be so like one of us, even the weakest among us?

'Don't imitate the madman,' said an inner voice. 'You would be as mad as he.'

'That,' he said at last,' is a matter between God and myself.'

He thought the commissar was going to choke.

'You shot at your son and you only think about this God of yours. But what about the French laws?'

The commissar in his clemency was prepared not to send him to prison (at least, not right now, he had said in an aside to the interpreter), but in the meanwhile he was confiscating his gun. The interpreter condescendingly added: 'It's customary to write a letter to the commissar, when you get back home, thanking him for his kindness.'

It was over at last! The commissar turned towards the interpreter and was speaking to him calmly, with even a smile at the corner of his mouth. The storm had quickly subsided. The father had ceased to understand anything.

'The commissar asks why you aren't curious to know where he got all his information from.'

'I don't want to know,' said the father. 'A man's life and what he does concern only God and himself.'

'The administrator says that as you seem to be a good fellow...'

The father opened his eyes wide. Were they going to return his ration-cards and let him keep his gun?

'... he's going to tell you.'

So that was it? 'But I'm not asking anything.'

The trooper did not translate that.

'It was Toudert, your cousin,' said the administrator. 'He even gave me the complete list of the members of your family, so that you couldn't keep back any ration-cards. But I see you're honest – you've given me all of them.'

The desk, the commissar, the interpreter suddenly vanished behind the mist which swamped his vision. The discordant voices of thousands of *muezzins* shouted something in his ears. He did not know what it was to feel unwell. He now thought he was going to faint.

He groped round the room two or three times without finding the door. He stumbled against chairs, walls – especially walls – and the interpreter, like a bee bumping against a window to get out into the sunlight beyond.

'You're in a hurry,' said the commissar.

He rang. An obsequious young man with bent back and drooping shoulders appeared at the door.

'See if he's paid his taxes.'

As it happened the father had not paid them that year. Food came first, and even for that there was not enough money.

'But I can mortgage my field – or sell it ...'

The commissar asked which field he meant, and when he heard that it was the Timezrit anger once again almost stifled the phrases that he gabbled in one breath. The trooper translated that the father was a dishonest man (he saw the father's head drop as though he had received a blow).

'I will pay the taxes,' he said, 'very soon.'

'The commissar says that you're dishonest because you've already mortgaged the Timezrit to Toudert; and besides, even when you've let him have the field, you'll still be far from having paid him all you owe him, and that you are completely in his power.'

The father saw the bent fingers of the commissar tighten convulsively round an imaginary neck.

All this was true, but since the commissar knew about it how could he possibly ask him to pay his taxes?

'The commissar says that you'd better mortgage your house.'

'It's a tumbledown old place. It wouldn't interest anyone.'

The commissar swung round suddenly. 'Yes – Toudert! Just the person. And an honest man too – yes, exactly what's needed.'

The commissar's shoulders shook with a silent laugh but no sign of it appeared on his face; only his eyes puckered up in an odd sort of way.

'You're a poor creature, the poorest of the poor. You're nothing but a rag in Toudert's hands, that he could tear to bits if he wasn't honest. To the administration you're just a worm that I could crush, if I didn't fear God – and as for your children, those brats of yours, you're bringing them up to act against France. You'd better look out.'

'Now,' said the interpreter, 'you can go.'

He went out shaking his head, completely dizzy. All evening he wandered about the deserted market-place, where famished dogs were fighting over bones in the stink of offal dung. It was late when he started walking back to Ighzer, too stupefied to feel angry. He wanted to return home alone and late at night so as to meet no one, see nothing, have nothing to say; yet, at the same time, he longed to reach home to sleep and forget, to sink deep into oblivion; to be rid of this burden weighing so heavily on his shoulders and stifling his lungs, just to think of nothing and to fall asleep. He quickened his pace. The lanes were empty, the night was studded with stars. The call of the jackals in the valley below came to his ears like distant sounds heard in a dream. He began stupidly to count the ash trees along the lane, without being very sure which lane it was.

When a tall, round-shouldered man jumped out from behind a bush he was counting: sixty-two, sixty-three. He started on sixty-four and fumbled instinctively around his belt, but no one carries a weapon to market. He drew back, automatically returned the greeting of the man who was barring the way, and tried hastily but in vain to gather his wits.

Yet the man there in front of him was Raveh-ou-Hemlat, the *amin* of Ighzer and mayor of the village; and to whom he had not spoken a word, because their families had for centuries belonged to two different *sofs*, for more than thirty years – ever since the day when the village assembly had chosen Raveh as *amin*.

'After we have finished our talk,' said the *amin* when they were sitting down, 'you will return to your clan and I to mine.'

The father felt the tightness round his chest easing. How good it was to be dealing with a real man.

'Our village,' said Raveh, 'is older than yesterday. The saints and the traditions of our ancestors have preserved it throughout the centuries. For thirty years now, it is I whom the will of God has chosen to watch over it. If the days of Ighzer are numbered, I intend it not to be while I'm in charge. Amen!'

An ox bellowed faintly in its slumbers or perhaps from a distance.

'Sliman your son, through the medium of Toudert, has asked for the hand of my daughter. Are they both out of their senses, or is it I who am too old for this new age?'

Somewhere in the night a baby called for its mother.

The father listened. Was it written that tonight the world would sink into oblivion?

'Your son Sliman is young; but Toudert, your cousin Toudert, is not a child any more. Now, when I refused to give my consent, your cousin Toudert, rich and elderly, asked me for Yakout for his son, and the ground did not open up and swallow him.'

The father went on his way with his head in a whirl, heavy with sleep and shame. Without a doubt, tonight would see the end of the world. First the enormous landslides and then, just before the smouldering light of dawn, the avenging angel appearing on the piles of ruins to sound his trumpet. . . .

His world began to crumble that night. Until then, moral values and all things that matter had been as inflexible as iron to him. There is the Almighty and there are men. Each man receives his destiny from God. It was He who had ordained the father's poverty, but poverty is no disgrace; only to lose one's honour is. Because all was inflexible, everything was simple too; the traditions of our ancestors hold the serene constancy of truth. All else is false. Arezki ought to marry Mekioussa after the death of Mohand, Sliman ought to find a bride within the clan of the Ait-Wandlous, because that is how it had been for centuries. The commissar ought to watch over the happiness of men and Toudert be generous and true because his wealth, which is a gift from God, obliges him to be.

MOULOUD FERAOUN

An Episode from
Les Chemins qui Montent

[*Time: mid-1950s. Place: a village in Kabylia. Dehbia and her widowed mother, Melha, are converts to Christianity, and poor. They have recently returned to live in Melha's native village. She is concerned about her daughter's future, and has already refused the offer of a wealthy old villager to marry Dehbia. Melha goes to work for another well-off family, the Ait-Slimane. One of the sons, Mokrane, makes overtures to Dehbia.*]

If there was one young man in the village whom Dehbia detested more than any other, it was Mokrane. She could hardly bear meeting him. He had a way of looking at her, of undressing her with his eyes, that made her furious. Even when he caught sight of her from a distance, he would stare at her unblinkingly with his big, black, flashing eyes. He was quite unconcerned that other people should notice, or that it embarrassed the girl; indeed, he seemed to want to annoy her, to convey to her in this way his bad temper as well as his desire. Did his bad temper result from wanting her so much, or did his desire spring from the scorn that he openly showed for the Christian girl? The Christian girl whose beauty tormented him and shocked his fanatical Muslim mind. . . . In his view, she deserved to be mercilessly raped. And he felt that he could accomplish such a pious act in a fit of rage. Dehbia hated him instinctively, and was even a little afraid of him. But apart from that stare, a gesture or two, and some rude remarks, there was really nothing she could hold against him. Besides, those were things that any girl might hold against any young man. So there was just that stare of his. She could not stand it; although nothing vexed her so much as indifference on the part of young men, she would rather pass a man who turned his head away than Mokrane with his cruel smile and glittering eyes. However, when they chanced to meet in a lonely spot, his heart seemed to sink; the smile froze stupidly and his look wavered, and she left him standing, her face hard and frowning. She did not glance back to see where he went. But she had learned one thing; that however vicious he might be, she could stand up to him. In a word, she was not scared of him.

When Melha started working for the Ait-Slimane family as a water-carrier, he pretended not to notice this new connection. Dehbia, who felt rather humiliated and upset by it, affected complete indifference and resolved never to set foot in the Ait-Slimanes' house. She returned her most sulky look to his expressionless smile. So the moment was badly chosen for him to try to kiss her. But how could anyone make that donkey understand the meaning of pride, a girl's honour, and tact! Well, he got what he asked for when he arrived with a dish of *kuskus*, his silly face beaming with desire.

'This is for your mother,' he murmured, holding out the dish.

As she took it and gave him a little smile, as though to forgive his unseemly behaviour in the past, he suddenly seized her by the waist. She dropped the plate and gave him a violent push that sent him hard against the wall ten feet away. He rubbed his shoulder without a word and went off seething.

At heart, she was pleased at having taught him a lesson. He no longer had any effect on her. She was greatly afraid that her mother might complicate matters, but she could not resist telling her about it, and in such a way that it appeared worthy of praise.

Despite the flaming row that Melha had with the Ait-Slimane couple, and the slander that the old woman spread about the 'two unbelievers' whom the Devil had sent to Ighil-Nezman to lead both young and old astray, Dehbia bore Mokrane no ill will. She was curious to meet him again, to steal a look at his sly features or, as she passed by the *djema*,[1] hear him make some

[1] Village meeting-place. (Tr. n.)

daring remark about young men's virility or the fire in their loins. Then, she thought to herself, she would adopt her most seductive attitude and, if she had the chance, would retort with a hurtful allusion that he could not fail to understand. The thought of this little game, into which Mokrane was drawing her, began to amuse her; for he was really too ugly, and she would enjoy mocking at him like a mischievous little imp. He was thick-set, with a big head, a great gash of a mouth, and the kind of eyes that frightened children. However closely he shaved, there were always little black bristles darkening his sun-tanned face. His big hands gave a false impression of strength, for he was no taller than she. If anything, he was below average height for a man. He was not much liked by the young people because he seemed to them to be behind the times, and had adopted all his mother's superstitions as well as the aversions and hypocrisy of his father. A worthy scion of the Ait-Slimanes, in fact, one who would live up to their reputation! He was tolerated only because he was rich and might help you out with a loan. He was not very communicative, and always worked alone in the family fields, which were his responsibility.

There was an irritating obstinacy in his approaches to Dehbia that made her long to hit him, to scratch his eyes out, and bite his tanned face.

She thought he would leave her alone after all the scandal. He might hate her, but would turn his attentions elsewhere, with his hungry look that took away your appetite, all pleasure in being beautiful and knowing yourself desirable.

'We'll soon see whether he got the message,' Dehbia said to herself.

She saw him again a few days later, at the *djema*. But there were a lot of people about, and Dehbia went by with the other girls, her pitcher on her shoulder, not daring to look round. But she knew that he was there. Just as she was crossing the square, a youth she thought better of called out in a bantering tone:

'Hey, Mokrane! It's still only spring, so don't think the fig's ripe yet. The fresh fig isn't for you!'

Mokrane made no reply, and Dehbia felt annoyed with the other. 'Besides,' she thought, 'I'm not for him, nor for you. You're silly idiots, all of you.' She felt cheapened at being compared to a fruit ripe for the taking. That was how they thought of love, these village yokels! When she got home, she looked at herself in the glass complacently. A peach! Now that would have pleased her. She would not have minded being called a peach. But he had said 'a fig', the idiot!

For the next few days Mokrane no longer looked out for her as she passed, as though he really wanted her to forget about him. But then he happened to appear some way off, by the fountain in one of their fields. She saw him there one day, and on the following days. Once he was up a cherry tree that was beginning to show ripe fruit, another time he was standing by the door of the shack where he stacked the hay; and on one occasion he was in the lane, busily engaged on mending a break in the hedge.

He always had his back turned as the girls approached, and when they had passed he went off and started on some other work. Dehbia was the only one to notice his little tricks. To make her presence known, she usually laughed loudly at some silly joke or daringly uttered a coarse word which made the others laugh. He was certainly not to be feared. He was pretending to be shy now, and trying to make her feel sorry for him; but he was just a hypocrite, and she detested him as much as ever.

'Perhaps he thinks I'm taking notice of him,' she told herself.

She stayed at home for two days and her mother did the water-carrying. But all the time Dehbia was longing to know whether he had shown himself along the path to the fountain, though she refrained from asking her mother, and never knew. On the third day she went down alone to fill her pitcher, at a time when there was usually no one at the fountain.

'He'll never think of waiting for me at this hour of day. And when the others come along later, he can go on looking out for me.'

However, Mokrane was near the shack, hard at work cutting up wood. She walked past unconcernedly, but noticed that he stopped work to stare at her, his face wide with surprise and his chopper held in the air as though in tribute.

'He sickens me, he really does,' she kept saying to herself, hurrying to reach the fountain.

Two old women arrived, and soon a little group had gathered round.

One afternoon, when she felt sure of finding him posted at one or the other of his chosen positions, Mokrane was not in sight. Dehbia instinctively glanced from the shack to the big ash tree, then from the cherry tree to the grapevine. There was no sign of him. She felt a slight disappointment, an emptiness in her heart.

'Get on!' she snapped at the young woman in front of her. 'Get on, or let me pass, you're dropping to sleep.'

'We've plenty of time, girl. You're in a hurry all of a sudden.'

Someone remarked that Mokrane had let them down this time, and they all burst out laughing. Dehbia reddened, and kept quiet. She wondered whether they thought he came specially to see her.

But she reassured herself: 'They're all too stupid. Besides, a fool like him . . .'

As they were all returning to the village, they saw Mokrane standing outside a door. It was market-day, and he was wearing a white *gandoura* over his dark jacket, with his *burnous* slung over his shoulder. He seemed to be waiting for someone to come out of the house. He turned his back on the women and edged close against the door to let them pass. Then he shouted to someone inside:

'Hurry up! You know I've only just come back from market. I haven't even been able to go and look at the cherries!'

But no one came to the door, and Dehbia felt sure that his words were for her benefit, as a kind of excuse.

The emptiness in her heart vanished. Everything was explained, all was in order. But she gave no sign, just said to herself once more, 'How he sickens me.'

One morning, Melha came back from the fields at about ten o'clock and dropped a bundle of dry sticks by the door. Then she wiped her face with her veil and looked sadly at her daughter, who was carefully rolling some barley-flour in a big wooden dish.

'Well, that's that,' she said casually. 'Mokrane got engaged to Ouiza n'Ait-Hamouche yesterday evening. I heard the women singing as I came past. Everyone's talking about it in the village.'

'What's that to me, Mother?' Dehbia replied with a shrug. 'Good for Ouiza!'

The evening before Mokrane became engaged to Ouiza, his father had told him about it and even asked his opinion. 'In an ordered society, my son,' he went on to say, 'everyone keeps his place and stays in his position. Otherwise, where would the Ait-Slimanes be now? Honour, religion and the family make for an ordered society. We are an old family, and so are the Ait-Hamouches. We have some property, the Ait-Hamouches are rich. We have men in the family, Ouiza has three brothers who are doing well in France, and they will be your brothers, too, when you go back there. All things considered, son, Ouiza is an excellent girl, and you will take her for your wife.'

Mokrane had complied because his father had gone on talking all evening, with the dish of *kuskus* in front of him, while Mokrane's elder brother and his wife kept giving similar little sharp nods of approval. Mokrane could not think of any objection because his mother had seen to everything, the dowry had been secretly arranged with his future mother-in-law, other advantages had been promised and the whole affair should go off smoothly. In fact, all that was left to Mokrane to do was to be happy because order, religion, honour and the family decreed that he should be happy, and to go and bestow a grateful kiss on his father's head, kiss his mother, wish everyone good-night, then go to bed and dream about Ouiza, as now that the choice had been made he must start thinking honourably about his wife and falling discreetly in love with her.

He gradually calmed down and went about his daily tasks with enthusiasm, thinking that in just a few days' time he would be a married man, have a woman of his own, and be living in the room above his brother's. There would soon be one more married man in the village, another sensible man able to start a family and bring up children. Who knows? Perhaps in a year's time ... The prospect of becoming a family man quite dispelled his doubts, and when he returned home at the end of the day it was Ouiza who occupied his thoughts.

He remained in this state of mind until the wedding day. Not only did he avoid Dehbia, he dismissed her from his mind. At least, every time her image rose before him, he made an irritable gesture like someone chasing away a persistent fly when trying to concentrate. It was all over, Dehbia was nothing more than a fly. Except that a fly is easily squashed and then you are left in peace, whereas the image of Dehbia was always slyly out of reach; and she herself could not always be avoided, he was bound to meet her in the village street, and then could but give her a cool glance while still wanting her.

The wedding went off very well. The village of Ighil-Nezman was not often the scene of such festivities. Two old families were being united, two influential families. Jealousies were either suppressed or transformed into hypocritical joy. No one was forgotten, all the poor of the village were invited to a meal of *kuskus*, and a dish was sent to every widow who could not attend. There was also a slap-up dinner for the village elders and other important guests; and Mokrane's brother, who was the parish clerk and special constable, proudly led them in procession through the village so that everyone could see them. The women's festivities lasted all night. They were allowed to dance and sing as much as they liked, while their menfolk stayed in the village café and the young men took charge of Mokrane and tried to make him drunk. And Mokrane, who had never before touched alcohol, got well and truly drunk, to the great delight of his mother who had thought he was incapable of it.

The following evening, he 'went into' his wife, as custom demanded. He had waited until after nightfall, and all was dark and silent in the village. Everyone was about to go to bed or was already asleep. Half a dozen of Mokrane's friends had insisted upon staying with him until the last. Now they were egging him on, encouraging him to 'go in', for he was somewhat agitated.

'Don't hesitate,' they told him. 'Get in there straight away, otherwise you're done for. Get in, and then fire your gun to let us know it's done. You don't need to stay with her all night, come out afterwards and we'll go back to the café until morning. She'll manage.'

'No', said Mokrane. 'I'll fire my gun, but I shan't come out again. Don't wait for me.' He was not at all certain of being able to 'get in' straight away, and he preferred to send them away.

'Very well. But in that case, hurry up and get the fritters and eggs for us.'

The fritters and eggs were another essential custom, a gift to one's pals who were not getting married; otherwise, tradition gave them the right to toss stones on to the roof, to break a few tiles, and even jeer outside the door, all of which was designed to prevent the bridegroom from carrying out what was expected of him, and if possible to make him a figure of ridicule for ever.

'Yes, you're right about the fritters. But in return, keep an eye open to see no one throws stones, will you?'

'Don't worry, we'll look out. Now, get on with it. Once you've fired your gun, nobody will think about disturbing you. So buck up with the shot!'

'And don't be put off by her attitude,' added the slyest among them. 'She's the one to be afraid. Got it? Put on a stern, harsh face. Look, like this! Talk tough, and don't start entreating her. Once you do that, you're done for.'

When he went inside he glanced doubtfully at the gun standing ready near the door, then shouted in a wrathful voice, 'Hurry up and give me the basket!'

But he stood looking at the floor, and could not have said what she looked like, where she was in the room nor what she was doing. The light from the oil-lamp was dazzling him, or else it was some confounded mist veiling everything. He got the basket in his face, seized it and went out saying in a shaky voice, 'And see you get the tea ready!'

He heard her reply with great complacency 'I know I have to get the tea. It's all ready.'

'That's a bad start,' he thought as he hurried off to his friends. 'Where's my pluck? I'm just being stupid!'

He did not linger at the *djema*, having made up his mind to put himself to the test at once. He found Ouiza reclining among some cushions on the bed and calmly looking through the picture-postcards that he had pinned on the walls a few days previously, to decorate the room; she had coolly taken them down again. They were pictures of lovely girls with scarlet cheeks and golden hair, smiling broadly at all admirers.

'Do you know them?' she asked, looking straight at him.

'Ye-es. They're Parisians.'

Standing there in front of her, he felt ill at ease under that unflurried look. Her face was powdered, her hands and feet were dyed with henna, and she was wearing two necklaces. She was sitting on the bed with her new clothes draped around her, and he thought she seemed awkward in all that get-up. But it was not his clothes that were making him feel awkward. He dared not sit down nor go nearer to her. He did not know what to do, and waited in the vague hope that she would have the goodness to break the ice. But Ouiza made no move.

'That gun is getting on my nerves,' he muttered. 'And the others are waiting . . .'

'What for?'

'For me to fire a shot.'

'Well then, fire it.'

This seemed a brilliant idea, to let off his gun beforehand. It would cause the young men to go away, and indicate to one and all that the deed was done. And his mother would hear, be pleased, and think: 'Well, that's that. My son's a man now.'

Then he would have all the night before him. So he picked up the gun, and Ouiza put her hands over her ears.

'Now we'll be left in peace,' he said after firing a shot.

'Yes, we'll be left in peace,' Ouiza agreed, still looking at the postcards.

Silence fell between them again. He was thinking that the shot which had set his parents' minds at rest, compelled him to act; and as this idea grew, he became more disturbed.

'I must do it, I must,' he kept telling himself. 'Luckily, the night is long. I've plenty of time.'

He tried to draw close to her, but she moved away, smiling and blushing.

'But I've fired the shot!' he exclaimed angrily.

'You shouldn't have.'

'And what about those waiting to hear it?'

'Then you should have.'

'Don't laugh at me, daughter of Ahmed! I've got a bad temper, you know. Pour out the tea.'

She made no reply, and poured the tea. Again he tried to draw near, even attempting to take her arm. She put the teapot down in front of him, and went and sat on the bed with her back to him.

'She's not giving in, that's quite clear,' he thought. 'She'll make me look a fine fool if I don't do something. Good God, am I a man, or what?'

He drank his tea by himself, a dark look on his face to indicate to her that he had decided to put an end to the business. But he was very much put out at having fired his gun and by Ouiza's hostile attitude. She did not seem afraid of him, yet she continued to hold him off, pretended not to understand, and altogether refused to . . . help him.

'I'll grab her suddenly, shut her mouth, and in a matter of seconds . . .'

The trouble was, he felt no urge, was almost indifferent. He assumed a grave, solemn air, as though at a meeting of the village elders at the *djema*. Ouiza began to feel nervous. She was probably expecting some bold move, a sudden onslaught such as every bride fears and hopes for. She prudently got between the sheets and lay down quietly. He was being left to manage. She was not even maintaining speaking terms and in all likelihood was beginning to despise him.

Mokrane's irritation turned to despair, and the despair to panic.

He took a half-bottle of anisette from a shelf, poured himself a large glassful, drank it off neat, then blew out the lamp.

'Now we'll see about it,' he said to himself. It was just a manner of speaking.

He groped his way into bed and lay down beside her. He would wait in the dark for the right moment, and give her no warning.

'It must be done, it must,' he kept telling himself. His head was going round and round. . . . He smiled at his stupidity. . . . 'Of course it's easy. There's not one of my pals who wouldn't like to be here in my place, the dirty dogs! I've got a wife, I have. As pretty as a doll. Oh, this is fine. I'm in luck.'

His head grew heavy and his body went slack. Nothing seemed to matter any more. His eyelids drooped, and he ceased to worry. He had not slept for two nights.

He awoke with a start, his throat constricted with anguish, and peered about in the dark. The blood rushed to his face. He felt an overwhelming urge, and cast himself furiously on the sleeping Ouiza. Before she was properly awake, the deed was done. She uttered a little cry but was unable to break free. He rose in triumph, and said haughtily as he went to the door: 'You can weep, daughter of Ahmed. I'm a man, I am!'

He slammed the door behind him. Just then, their cock began to crow. Dawn was breaking; he had managed it just in time. He ran off. The morning air revived him, and he laughed for joy as he went down to the shack near the fountain; he intended to lie in the hay and catch up on his sleep.

But he woke up a few hours later and began thinking about his feat. Life seemed good; he imagined his mother, his sister-in-law, his mother-in-law and other women hurrying to see and not being disappointed, having verified that everything had gone as it should, that the wedding was over and there was now one more man, one more married woman in the village. And, in the near future, a baby who would be growing up while others were coming along. . . . 'Mustn't look too far ahead,' he thought.

The image of Dehbia suddenly came to his mind. He had not really forgotten the Christian girl, and even when lying beside

Ouiza he had thought of her, despite himself. He had imagined her lovely smile and for a moment he had reflected that if she had been there beside him, then he might have been more forth-coming. He began to feel a little sorry for her.

'If I meet her,' he decided, 'I'll give her a special look. It will be a way of staying faithful to her, at least with my eyes. Without wronging Ouiza, of course.'

As it happened, he met her on his way back to the village. She was going down to the fountain with her mother and another woman. He felt ill at ease as they approached; Melha always pulled a horrid face at him whenever she met him, so that he preferred to avoid her.

'What'll it be like this time!' he wondered. 'She's sure to insult me. Oh well, press on.'

He went on. The two women passed him. He had turned his back to them. Dehbia, having seen him approaching, had lagged behind. When he started on his way again, she was just in front of him. His heart beat wildly, and he ventured a smile.

'You skunk!' she flung at him, in French.

It was as though she had spat in his face, and he automatically wiped his cheek.

'The little beast!' he thought. 'She's eaten up with jealousy. So she's still after me. And all I wanted was to take a rise out of her, that's all.'

But he was no longer in a hurry to get home, and his appetite had completely vanished.

ASSIA DJEBAR

A chapter from
Les Impatients

[*The narrator and heroine, Dalila, lives in a large house in Algiers with her stepmother, Lella, her brother Farid and his wife, Zineb, and various aunts and cousins. Dalila has been seeing a young man, Salim, without the knowledge of her relatives. She has just met with an accident in the street, after a row with Salim, and is now recovering at the apartment of her married sister, Cherifa, as it is quieter there than at the family house, full of chattering women. Moreover, Dalila has already clashed with her stepmother, Lella.*]

I stayed at my sister's for a few more days. She was more relaxed now, and came and sat at my bedside to keep me company. To pass the time, we sometimes invented games to play with her small daughter, Sakina, and these made us laugh a lot. At such times I caught a youthful gleam in Cherifa's eyes. I should have liked to tell her . . . On occasion, she could display an ingenuousness that would have made her more appealing. In the late afternoons, when nearly everyone had gone out, I sat on the balcony, in a chaise-longue. From there, I could see a narrow street along one side of a square. And so I dreamed away the time.

One evening, I noticed a man standing against a doorway in the street and looking in my direction. It was Salim. I felt my heart begin to thump. At that distance, only his figure was recognizable; I could barely distinguish the look on his face. We remained like that, in a remote tête-à-tête, for a long time, until nightfall. Now and again a passer-by looked at Salim standing there quite still, then glanced across at the building. I never took my eyes from the spot down below where a man was watching over me.

Several days in succession, I went on to the balcony to wait for evening to come. I never knew what time Salim would arrive; but about the middle of the afternoon I would wake from my siesta with a start – 'He's there,' I told myself. The certainty made me restless in bed. I called Cherifa, and she helped me up with a gentleness that in my eagerness I failed to appreciate. She made me comfortable on the balcony, putting a pillow behind my head and another under my feet. I longed for her to go, so that I could look down at the street.

She went, and slowly and discreetly I turned my head towards the street. He was there. To find that I had sensed aright filled me with a serene assurance that set me apart from the rest of the household; I entered a domain where only he and I existed. The hours went by. He did not move. I could not see his expression, just his hair falling limply over his forehead. But I recognized the dear way he looked at one, with head lowered and his restless eyes peering from under bushy eyebrows. In the end, all I could make out in the busy street was that face, so near, so truly near. I was at peace, wanting nothing. I felt like lying back in my chair and falling asleep with his eyes still on me.

I could sense by the way he was standing still and gazing at me that he would have liked to eliminate the distance between us. But I was satisfied as it was, filled with an undemanding, simple happiness by being simply aware that he sought me. And I felt warmly grateful to this man who was giving me that happiness. I let myself be loved.

One morning, Zineb came in brightening my room with her smile. I was so pleased to see her.

'It's so boring at home,' she said. 'I miss you . . .'

Away from her husband, away from the other women, she soon recovered her girlish looks when with me. A frank intimacy grew up between us. Young Arab women have an unsuspected store of romanticism; thrown too abruptly into a man's arms, they rarely find their wounded innocence again. And their husbands never know their exalted, youthful expressions – only their hard, dry looks of a submissive animal, a feeble creature.

We chatted away very pleasantly for some time. She gave me all the gossip with childish glee, and so devoid of spite that I began to take an interest in what she said.

'When I'm at home,' I told her, 'nothing ever seems to happen . . .'

'But it's you, dear, who never notice anything! You're too wrapped up in yourself.'

She suddenly drew her chair close to the bed and started to whisper, her eyes aglow.

'I'll tell you something that concerns you – but promise not to repeat it to anyone.'

'That concerns me . . . ?'

I showed no eagerness. She liked being pressed.

'It's a conversation about you, between Farid and Lella. When we'd finished our meal, Farid made a sign to me to leave them together. But I couldn't help listening from the gallery . . .' She bent nearer, and went on in an even lower voice. 'Someone has asked for you in marriage. . . . Do you know what his name is?' she said eagerly.

'What?' I asked languidly.

'El Hadj. Salim El Hadj. It seems that you know his cousin. El Hadj was the man who drove you to hospital after your accident. Presumably, even in that state, you must have pleased him. . . .'

For a moment, I was speechless. But I had to know more.

'And Lella? What did Lella say?'

'She thought he's too old for you.'

'Farid told her his age, then?'

'No, I don't think so . . .' Her mind jumped on a bit. 'Anyway, this morning, I just had to ask Thamani, and she told me all about him. He's handsome and . . .'

I cut her short. 'Look, can you tell me what they said, from the beginning – what Farid said, and Lella? Yes, tell me exactly everything that Lella said, can you?'

She started from the beginning.

Salim had not made his proposal in the traditional manner. 'I could merely ask for her hand in marriage,' he had said to Farid. 'But first, I should like to have your permission to make her acquaintance and talk with her. I want her to be free to choose.' Farid had repeated this to Lella. He knew the other to be sound, and – he had added – he liked the man's honesty. Of course, such a request had its dangers. 'Besides,' he had continued, 'Dalila is so odd at times, so unpredictable, that she might not accept him, might meet him and then refuse him. Who knows?' He had added, in a pessimistic tone: 'Once you start asking girls of today what they think, they take themselves seriously and do foolish things. But I like El Hadj's honesty. And he's a good match from every point of view – family, social background, situation . . .'

I interrupted Zineb's account. 'What did Lella reply? Tell me what she had to say.'

'She remained silent until Farid had finished. Then she said: "I consider it's too soon for Dalila to think of getting married. She is young, and in my opinion it would be a pity not to let her finish her studies. An early marriage would make her like all the other wives. As you know, Farid, I'm very ambitious for Dalila. She's intelligent, and has a future ahead of her. Recently, when she talked so enthusiastically about those meetings of other girls that she went to, I could see what her future will be. She needs to become a woman capable of facing up to numerous social responsibilities. Marriage, at this time, would stifle her character. I want her to be happy, and she will be. But I want her to have great qualities too, to be a woman who will set an example." '

Zineb had gradually adopted Lella's manner of talking. I could easily imagine the scene.

'I'm the one to decide what I want to be,' I exclaimed. ' "My future, my character" – nothing but words. She hasn't the right to mould me as she thinks fit. I shall be what I wish.'

I stopped, I wanted to know the rest. The rest was important. I could just hear Lella's fine phrases, and, in spite of myself, was fascinated by the pride in her words.

'What did she say about Salim?'

'Salim?'

'About the man . . . about him . . .'

'She made a few remarks about his age, first. Then she maintained that his proposal was unacceptable, that there was only danger in it. "I prefer," she went on, "the traditional manner, whatever this gentleman thinks. Just because Dalila will have exchanged a few words with him doesn't mean that she'll be capable of deciding whether the man is suited to her. Marriage is a serious matter, and she isn't mature enough to enter on it alone. If we agree to marry her, then it's up to us to decide. But if, as I would rather do, we let her continue her studies, it'll be a few years before she's able to shoulder her responsibilities."

' "Yes, of course," Farid agreed. "But Dalila will be going to the University. If we refuse El Hadj, what is there to stop him getting to know her, if he's set on it, outside our control?"

' "You're forgetting Dalila," replied Lella, "and how she ought to behave. If she carries on with her studies, I mean to see that she keeps her self-respect. I don't want her to speak to any man while she's at university." '

I kicked at the bedclothes. 'That's it – to her, keeping your self-respect is not speaking to men!'

'But let me go on,' said Zineb. 'She's decided to talk to you before the university year begins. "I'll explain to her that as she will belong to the first generation of girls to go to university, she has a duty to follow a strict, if not rigid, line of conduct. Her responsibilities to others are great. She must think first of all of her reputation." That's what Lella said.'

I longed to exclaim to that woman: 'It's easy to talk of responsibilities, reputation, and setting an example! What I want first of all is to be myself. That's all. I'm not like you, trying to splash my self-respect and virtue on to others, while . . .'

'While what?' prompted Zineb, intent on my words. I had spoken my thoughts aloud.

'While Lella talks of virtue, what matters to me is my purity; while Lella talks of my responsibilities to others, what concerns me are my responsibilities to myself.'

'I don't understand,' Zineb sighed. 'Aren't they the same thing?'

'No, I don't think so. . . . Anyway, that's what I'll tell her when she speaks to me about it. I'll even tell Farid . . .'

'Neither of them will speak to you about it. Farid won't turn down El Hadj, but he'll make an excuse of your youth and your studies. He'll ask him to raise the matter of this marriage again in a year's time. By then, you'll know whether you want to continue with your studies or abandon them and get married. Lella insisted that nothing should be said to you now. At your age, apparently, it might upset you. Don't say anything about this to anyone, please. If they were to know . . .'

I gave a slight smile. 'I'd have heard, in any case.'

'You'd have heard about it?'

'Oh yes. And from Salim El Hadj himself. I know him, and I've often been out with him. If it weren't for my accident and not being able to get out since, I'd have known all about this. Whatever ideas Lella may have for my future, I decided about it long before she did.'

'You? You did?' Zineb had a scared look, suddenly seeing something new and dangerous in me. She was frightened.

'Frightened, Zineb? Are you frightened? For yourself or for me?'

'No, I think you're crazy. . . . I'd never have believed . . .'

'Listen, Zineb. One must learn to have courage.'

I was about to add – courage to decide for oneself, to make one's own decisions. But I realized that one first needed to be strong. The young woman who was hurrying away, who would avoid me in future, would always be frightened of taking a risk. And therefore she would never obtain from Farid, her husband, what she was always unconsciously craving for – the trusting, indulgent smile of a companion.

MALEK HADDAD

Extracts from
Je t'offrirai une Gazelle

[*Moulay is a lorry-driver for a Trans-Sahara Transport Company.
His father was a ruined Prince who had owned more palm trees than
there are illusions in the heart of a poem. Moulay is in love with
Yaminata, who is seventeen and worth twenty white camels.*

*Just before Moulay sets out on a journey across the desert,
Yaminata asks him to bring her back a gazelle, a live one, for
'gazelles are gazelles only when alive'.*

*But her father has received an offer of marriage from another
Arab, Kabeche, who is well in with the local French authorities . . .*]

'You'll have the number of camels you want . . .'

Yaminita's father hesitated. He saw piles of sacks of semolina
finer than the red sands of El-Barkat. He saw many loaves of
sugar and forests of green tea.

'I appreciate the honour you do to me, but my daughter is
very young . . .'

He dared not look Kabeche squarely in the face. He was not
impressed by this lame man. Fear and timidity are much the
same. Kabeche was an Arab who enjoyed the confidence of the
French commanding officer and the friendship of Lieutenant
Masson. And he did not let you forget it.

When fate has military headwear, it should be doubly dis-
trusted. Or else you must be very powerful in order to displease
it, and the more powerful to go against it.

The old man said again: 'My daughter is still very young.'

Kabeche was a realist. He believed that everything has its price.
He was unaware that what is without price is not for sale.

'I will add five camels.'

The father retorted – oh, timidly, in a low voice, as though to excuse himself: 'Adding five camels won't put five years on my daughter's age. . .'

The other looked annoyed. His bony face had gone white and there was a nasty glint in his eyes.

'I'll think about it,' said the father. 'Let me think it over.'

The tone was broken, defeated. To think over a proposal that you did not greet with enthusiasm is half-way to accepting it.

'Yes, that's right, that's most wise; think it over.'

This advice was a threat. The suitor – the spider weaving its web – was jubilant. On that day, so it is said, the turtle-doves refused to coo and the desert wind rose in protest.

'Never, never!'

On the little terrace of beaten earth, Yaminata sought the comfort of her mother's arms. Her mother let her weep, and she wept for some time. When her sobbing had died away, Yaminata looked up; it was no longer the look of a child, she had wept for her love and her tears had conferred a sort of sudden majority upon her, a new maturity.

Her mother said tentatively: 'With Kabeche, you'll never know what it is to be hungry or cold.'

Yaminata went quite pale. 'I'd rather die . . .'

Gazelles are not to be trifled with.

'. . . . yes, I'd rather die.'

The words remained graven in their everlasting conviction.

At the new moon, Moulay would be back. The thought comforted the girl. Moulay would be here, as staunch and firm as the ramparts of the Koukoumen, the mountain range whose jagged tops were shimmering on the skyline. As firm as the red sandstone keep of the Turkish fort that could be seen in the distance. The time of the gazelles was only just beginning. Spiders weaving their evil would reap nothing for their patience and devil's strategy. There were indeed two ravens circling above the Koukoumen, but the sky was so blue and the ravens were so faultlessly outlined that there was no hint of danger, nothing to mar the moment.

Moulay would be back at the new moon. Evil would roam in vain. There remained just a slight upset, with a sharp after-taste of fear in Yaminata's mouth. And that small chest breathing awry. Her heart had taken up all the room in it.

It was about midday when Moulay realized that the end had come, that all was ended, was about to end.

Three days ago, he had insisted on making a detour to what he called 'the cemetery of cemeteries'.

It was near the top of a sand-dune; a strange death-camp, a kind of half-uncovered burial ground. Legend had it that, several decades ago, these unfortunates had left Tripolitania, fleeing from the boons of Mussolini. No one will ever know just what happened. But there they were, jumbled together in their last sleep, in the confusion of their panic. Little blue teapots, glass necklaces and cracked goat-skin bottles were lying on the sand, quite visible; and, a little apart, could be seen the almost intact face of a girl, with her red hair giving the startling impression of grass sprouting from the sand. The rest of her, still covered, was not so well preserved. Moulay never missed going this way, before tackling the O'Hannet dunes.

He had no reason for making this pilgrimage. It was not from curiosity. All unwittingly, he brought this girl with red hair back to life. He imagined her drinking milk or marvelling over a cheap necklace. The desert girl was in pursuit of poems. She seemed tiny and solitary, but important. Moulay's mate, Ali, never laughed at this spot. There, it was the sea twice over, death twice over, and silence twice over.

Moulay drove speedily away from the spot. They had to get as far as possible and camp for the night in the shelter of a dune.

A few hours after leaving the girl with red hair, Moulay became concerned at not finding the wheel-tracks that were his usual guide. He headed north-west. The landscape was frighteningly all familiar, the landscapes here being alike.

Ali had cheered up, and every now and then gave a great shout of '*Andik!* Look out!' as though crying defiance at the sky and the sand. Moulay, who was driving, made wide zig-zags in the hope of coming across the wheel-tracks; but without success. However, he was not yet greatly alarmed. The girl with red hair was singing in the engine, sometimes with Yaminata's voice.

The evening came. Night fell, a fine, lovely night and still fresh, then suddenly cold. Ali cooked their *charba*, meat and vegetable soup, in a pot as usual. But, later, Moulay shook his head when Ali passed the hookah to him. This was the first time Moulay had refused to smoke 'kif'. Yet he never abused it.

They were up and about very early. Moulay climbed the dune while his mate made some tea. From the top of the dune Moulay could see only other high dunes stretching to the distant horizon. 'I followed the wrong gap,' he admitted to himself.

Ali had said nothing. There was still enough petrol for two days' travel, and water for as long a time. God is great.

So is the Sahara.

The lorry was of no use any more. Nothing was of any use. They had drunk the warm water, the brackish water, the rusty water from the radiator. Now the music had begun in their heads. You no longer know what you're doing when about to die. There was the desert girl, a girl with red hair, holding out some lovely cool, sour milk, but it was too good to be true. She had no business to be there. She was one of the living. You could see her standing near the lorry, waving Yaminata's scarf and pointing to an oasis, scattering her laugh over the water. But Ali saw nothing, he said he could not see a thing. He had no laugh or shout left in him. There was just one idea in his mind – to drink, drink. . . . An idea oddly fixed in his gullet, in his very entrails. Ali's eyes were just two round blobs. He was nothing but his eyes; they were all you saw of his face.

Oh for a drink! Who knows, by thinking of God, by asking Him for water, who knows, God performs miracles. . . . God can do anything. But Moulay and his mate had no time to think of God. They were thirsty, they had no thought of praying. They had but one idea, to drink. You have to die in your bed to think of praying. You need to be in want of nothing to know how to die. In those conditions, anyone is in a position to meet death. You mustn't be out of your mind in order to die.

A drink. You should drink before dying. Dying is nothing. If needs must, I would agree to die after having a drink. A cunning trap . . .

At the foot of the dune there were now two lorries, three, a hundred, a whole herd of lorries. And these lorries were browsing on the red hair of the desert girl. There was sun everywhere, especially in the stomach. Sometimes there were rosy birds singing, birds which spoke Arabic. For there are birds that speak Arabic. There are even lorries that carry refrigerators. There are even umbrellas made of sugar.

The two men had gone round in circles all night, and the previous night, and the night before that. For ten years they had been going round in circles. They had always gone round in circles.

Ali was obsessed with his idea. He could taste snow. They sold crushed ice and lemon at Ouargla, crushed ice and lemon in little glasses, crushed ice and lemon that you ate with little spoons.

Well then!

Well nothing . . .

Moulay tried to stand up. He had not realized that he was crawling on all fours. There was a garden with a pond in it behind the town hall . . .

Well then!

Well nothing.

Yes. The sun has seen worse things than that. Or rather, the sun has never seen anything like it.

Say what you will, but a gazelle was rubbing its pointed muzzle against Moulay's cheek. Perhaps it was a real gazelle, perhaps it was a real gazelle that wasn't real. In any case, mirages do not speak.

The gazelle looked at Moulay. Moulay stretched out his hand. 'You've come for Yaminata, haven't you? Eh, you've come for Yaminata?'

The gazelle pondered this over before replying. Then she said: 'No, I've come for you.'

He said: 'You've got the same voice as Yaminata.'

And the gazelle said: 'It's you who have the same ears as when with Yaminata.'

Say what you will, perhaps it was a real gazelle, perhaps it was a real gazelle that wasn't real.

But she said: 'You can take me, if you like.'

And he said: 'I'd like to, Yaminata will be happy, she'll have a gazelle, a baby, a scarf . . .'

Well then!

Well nothing.

No, not that! Not that! Ali was trying to open his veins; he was thirsty, he wanted to drink his blood. But he did not have the strength to open his veins. His knife fell in the sand. It was small, that knife.

'Moulay, please, I implore you . . . Get it over, go on . . .'

Eyes like that could not be refused anything. A helping hand had to be given Ali.

What had to be done was to pick up the revolver, which weighed two tons. You had to lift the safety-catch. You had to get nearer to Ali . . .

You had to stop believing in God, in men, stop believing in lemon and ice in little glasses, in a pond in the town-hall garden.

'Moulay, please, I implore you . . . get it over, go on . . .'

They were Ali's last words. There was none of the usual peace of the everlasting on his face. Even in death he must have felt thirsty.

Moulay was alone now.

The gazelle had returned. It had rained in Moulay's head; spots of rain and flamenco. All the storms in the world would be needed for a drop of liquid other than blood to be squeezed from this spent body. Nevertheless, a tear came. God alone knows where it came from. There were palm trees, a red scarf, a demure young woman at the foot of Mount Koukoumen.

'I shall call him Moulay, after you,' Yaminata had said, putting her small hands on her small, still smooth, belly.

The gazelle approached closer to Moulay.

Say what you will, perhaps she was a real gazelle, perhaps she was a real gazelle that wasn't real. But nevertheless what she said was real, were real gazelle words.

'You must be mad, Moulay, to want to catch me. You have to believe in me, but you don't have to chase after me. You must be mad, Moulay, to want to catch me.'

The author ended:

'I don't know whether the gazelle was a real gazelle or a real gazelle that wasn't real, but nevertheless she regretted her words when Moulay turned upon himself the weapon that had delivered his mate.'

Yaminata was gazing at the approaching night. The Koukoumen was gazing at Yaminata. Her belly was slightly rounded. But it was not noticeable under the blue *gandoura*. It was slightly rounded all the same.

Yaminata had crossed her hands over her little rounded belly. She felt proud and heavy.

The gaze went farther than all the horizons. The heart went farther than the track across the desert.

The track told of nothing.

The cemetery knew things, those things that the track did not tell. The stars knew too; but the stars would not say anything.

There came a phrase, on the world's first page, that was thrilling and thoughtful. As thoughtful as a little rounded belly.

'If it's a boy, I shall call him Moulay.'

Then after a short silence: 'And if it's a girl? What shall I call her, if it's a girl? I'll ask Moulay. He knows everything . . .'

Moulay knew everything now. He knew why the red hair grew

in the sand. He knew what the eternal track knew and had no wish
to tell, what the stars knew and would not say to Yaminata.

To Yaminata, who knew that her little belly was rounded.

Gleanings from other pages

Being original, these days, consists of singing in a group to make
your voice heard.

It was a sad place, like all offices. They don't like work. They are
as sad as railway stations. But railway stations have an excuse –
they never travel.

A telephone ringing is like a child crying to have his toy back.
It's better to give way at once.

KATEB YACINE

Extracts from
Le Polygone Étoilé

[*Lakhdar has left Algeria to look for work in France. He gets a job as a builder's labourer at a town in the Rhône valley where a number of Algerians are working. In the evening, he sees one of them leaning over the bridge.*]

Lakhdar went up and greeted him. The other replied in Arabic. Things weren't too bad. You got used to it in the end. It was time to cook some spuds. They'd eat together, of course. Yes, from the same region. Son of a peasant at Akbou. Went to Algiers, but nothing doing. Here? It's better and it's worse. Not much of a place. A spirit-lamp, a tin saucepan, and only one chair. Lakhdar sat on the bed, gobbled up three-quarters of the pittance and sang until midnight.

'Sleep here in my room,' said Cherif. 'We'll only have to pay two hundred francs a week each. We shall move on before long. With your education, you won't remain a builder's labourer. And I'm fed up with it. The boss asks me to have a drink with him now. Says he has confidence in me – and gives me the hard jobs. Before we go to sleep, write a letter to my mother for me. Make her understand that the money here is even more worthless than over there. I can't send her anything for the time being. Brothers and sisters. Tell her I'll get married back home one of these days, but not to the girl she has chosen. Too thin. No, don't put that. Do your best to spin out the letter.'

The fat, bustling woman who kept the hotel always had with her a young girl of similar proportions who slammed the door in clients' faces. The woman was always yelling, or else she jabbered away: 'I can't understand why workmen keep the light on until after midnight. It's the Algerians, of course, who stay up all night like owls.'

Every night, Cherif had a moan: 'I'm on the cement-mixer. My arms are like jelly. I hope for your sake you don't get put on the pneumatic-drill. What gets me down, is the boss being so nice to me. A little more and he'll be lending me his wife, to ruin my health still more.'

'Be on the bridge at four tomorrow morning. You're being sent on another job. With a bonus on your week's wages.' He loitered on the river bank, smoking one cigarette after another from a new packet already half empty. Almost fell asleep on his feet. The bridge was deserted, swept by gusts of icy wind. His stale sweat seemed like another shirt, moist and stiff; he stamped his feet, huddled into his jacket, peering through the shredded curtain of dismal rain at approaching vehicles, splashed about in his rope-soled sandals, cursed, smoked, then ran. It was an open lorry. Only one of the faces at the back was familiar – Gigi. A labourer, age about fifty; wore clogs and corduroy trousers. A simple soul. 'Mind your heads' – the lorry had turned into a lane with overgrown, tangled hedges. The branches swished and the driver accelerated. Lakhdar was the last to jump down. There was a château with mossy, greenish walls and a steep roof. The slates had to be replaced by tiles. The owner had died. Nature was taking over.

There was a long ladder against one wall, a rope, a heap of mortar gone hard. The usual sight.

'We going to be working here long?'

'You never know, in the building trade. We'll be digging drains, next job.'

The contractor had arrived unnoticed. An energetic expression that was almost devout. Blue eyes – or were they red? Skinny. His face a network of wrinkles. Italian.

'Time to start work,' he said, and the ladder began to tremble.

. . . . .

Doesn't matter, man
He's an Algerian
who works hard
and eats nowt.

The rain, the end of the day, a chicken strutting aimlessly about the site, nodding its head and shutting one eye, and the two voices as the spades stirred the hardening mortar:

An Algerian
proletarian
who suffers and says nothing.
But now we'll have something to say!

[*Another character appears in the book, which is now concerned with the Algerian War of Independence.*]

Out-of-luck Hassan
5 feet 4
Eleven spells in prison
Whence his vast culture
On one occasion
In a bar
A Grand Gentleman
In riding habit
Jostled
Without a word of apology
An Arabo-Berber

Hassan looked around him, seized a box of
cheese lying on a table, tore off the lid, and
wrote on it in big letters: OUT-OF-LUCK HASSAN.

'Here is my card. No choice of weapons.'

He had begun his career at Souk-Ahras, using stolen cars, clearing the road ahead merely by driving like a madman, before heading straight at the objective, a police post, a sentry-box suddenly lacking a sentry, when he was reduced to such child's play, to say nothing of the farmhouses and crops set on fire and the blowing up of trains. . . . He recruited his men himself, often just for a single operation, and allowed them a free hand, provided they were capable of running with him, when the time came, the forty-odd miles from Souk-Ahras to the frontier, or vice-versa.

Out-of-luck Hassan?

Terribly highly-strung, the slightest thing made him jump as high as a tree (it was the spirits of traitors he had executed, people said), and he generally spent the idle hours swinging from branch to branch while listening to the conversation; he devoured cigarettes rather than smoked them, throwing the stubs where he ought not, so that he could pass the time by going and stamping them out. During meetings, he kept absentmindedly lifting the table. He considered every minute to be a waste, and the organization was hard put to get him out of the prisons into which his deeds landed him.

[*The novel ends with the writer beginning his life story.*]

Anyone who saw me, even from a distance, in the bosom of the family during my earliest years would probably have said that I would become a writer, or at least an ardent booklover, but if he had ventured to forecast the language I should write in he would have said without hesitation: 'In Arabic, like his father, his mother, his uncles and grandparents.' He should have been right, for so far as I can remember the first harmonies of the Muses flowed naturally for me, from the maternal source.

My father would flippantly turn prose into verse whenever he opened the *Commentaries* or *Muslim Law,* and my mother would often give him his cue, but then she had a natural gift for the theatre. What am I saying? She was a theatre in herself. I was her sole, enchanted audience when my father was away at some law court, from which he would return in a bantering or tragic mood, according to the outcome of his case.

All went well while I was in fleeting attendance at the Koranic school at Sedrata, near the Algerian frontier with Tunisia. . . . But when I was seven, my father suddenly made the irrevocable decision to cast me into the lion's mouth, in other words to send me to the French school. It was with a heavy heart that he said to me:

'Drop Arabic for now. I don't want you to be caught between two stools, like me. . . . French is the commanding language, and you must have a command of it. Leave everything that your mother and I have instilled in you from your earliest childhood. But once you've mastered the French language, you'll be able to come back to your beginnings again.'

That was the gist of what my father said. Did he really believe it himself?

My mother sighed; and when I embarked on my new studies and did my homework by myself, I would see her wandering about like a soul in torment. It was farewell to our intimate and childish theatricals, to our daily little plot against my father, retorting in verse to his satirical jests. . . . And all was set for drama.

After a slow and difficult start, I soon took to the foreign language; then I fell for a vivacious young school-teacher and even thought of doing all the sums in my Arithmetic book for her!

My mother was too sensitive not to be affected by this disloyalty towards her. I can still see her, all ruffled and offended, tearing me away from my books – 'You'll fall ill!' – and then saying to me one evening, in a candid but rather sad way, 'As I must stop distracting you from this other world of yours, teach me French then.' Thus will the trap of Modern Times close over my frail roots, and now I'm furious at my stupid pride that day when my mother sat down at my desk with a French newspaper, more distant than she had ever been, pale and still, as though the cruel schoolboy's little hand obliged her, since he was her son, to wrap herself in silence and even to follow him to the end of his effort and solitude – into the lion's mouth.

Since then, and even during the time I found favour with the school-mistress, I've never ceased to feel, deep within me, that second snapping of the umbilical cord, that inward exile which kept mother and son apart, torn from the murmur of blood and the reproachful sighs of a language secretly banished by a mutual agreement which was shattered as soon as made. Thus did I lose both my mother and her language, the only treasures that cannot be forgone – yet were nevertheless forsaken!

BIBLIOGRAPHY

Rachid Boudjedra
La Répudiation   Denoël 1969

Mourad Bourboune
Le Mont des Genêts   Julliard 1962
Le Muezzin   C. Bourgois 1968

Driss Chraibi
Le Passé Simple   Denoël 1953
Les Boucs   Denoël 1954
L'Ane   Denoël 1956
De Tous Les Horizons   Denoël 1958
La Foule   Denoël 1960
Succession Ouverte   Denoël 1962
Un Ami Viendra Vous Voir   Denoël 1967

Mohammed Dib
La Grande Maison   Seuil 1952
L'Incendie   Seuil 1954
Au Café   Gallimard 1955
Le Métier à Tisser   Seuil 1957
Un Été Africain   Seuil 1959
Baba Fekrane   La Farandole 1959
Ombre Gardienne (poetry)   Gallimard 1961
Qui Se Souvient de la Mer   Seuil 1962
Cours sur la Rive Sauvage   Seuil 1964
Le Talisman   Seuil 1966
La Danse du Roi   Seuil 1968

Assia Djebar
La Soif   Julliard 1957
Les Impatients   Julliard 1958
Les Enfants du Nouveau Monde   Julliard 1962
Les Alouettes Naives   Julliard 1967

Mouloud Feraoun
Le Fils du Pauvre   Seuil 1952
La Terre et Le Sang   Seuil 1953
Les Chemins qui Montent   Seuil 1957
Les Poèmes de Si-Mohand (essay)   Ed. de Minuit 1959
Journal, 1955–1962   Seuil 1962
Jours de Kabylie   Ed. Baconnier 1954
                                       re-issued Seuil 1968
Lettres à ses Amis   Seuil 1969

Malek Haddad
Le Malheur En Danger (poetry)   Nef de Paris 1956
La Dernière Impression   Julliard 1958
Je t'offrirai une Gazelle   Julliard 1959
L'Élève et La Leçon   Julliard 1960
Le Quai aux Fleurs Ne Répond Plus   Julliard 1961

Mohammed Khair-Eddine
Agadir   Seuil 1967
Corps Négatif   Seuil 1968
Soleil Arachnide   Seuil 1969

Mouloud Mammeri
La Colline Oubliée   Plon 1952
Le Sommeil du Juste   Plon 1955

Malek Ouary
Le Grain dans La Meule   Correa 1956

Ahmed Sefrioui
La Boite à Merveilles   Seuil 1954
Maroc   Hachette 1962
Le Chapelet d'Ambre   Seuil 1964

Kateb Yacine
Soliloques (poetry)   Bône 1946
Nedjma   Seuil 1956
Le Cercle des Représailles (plays)   Seuil 1959
Le Polygone Étoilé   Seuil 1966

Hacène Farouk Zehar
Peloton de Tête   Julliard 1966